1.99
E

WIRELESS TRANSMISSION
1882
1873

ATOMIC POWER
1900-05 1958

THE COMPUTER
1939 1954

THE TRANSISTOR
1948 1958

CRYOGENICS
1950 1968

THE NEW BIOLOGY
(GENETICS)
1952 1966-67

THE LASER
1958 1965

1966

D1180124

advances in communications, computerization, medicine and space exploration recorded over the past 15 years. The transistor is symbolic of the technology of our era: small, reliable, cool, all-pervasive.

1948	Development of transistor at Bell Laboratories.
1952	Transistorized hearing aids.
1952	Application of transistors to telephone communications.
1954	Transistorized military computer.
1954	Transistorized portable radio.
1958	Use of transistors in Explorer satellite.
1958	Installation of transistorized commercial computers.

CRYOGENICS

Experiments with low temperature or cryogenics date back to the early part of this century, but it was not until the 1950's that they became an important branch of the physical sciences. The phenomenon of superconductivity occurring at minus 420°F. is bringing revolutionary advances in power production and transmission, the space sciences, industry and medicine.

1950	B. T. Matthias' experiments in practical uses for cryogenics.
1954	Dudley Back's invention of "Cryoton" — thin film cryogenic switch.
1968	Plans prepared to convert Stanford University linear particle accelerator to a cryogenic facility.

THE NEW BIOLOGY (GENETICS)

Genetics go back to the experiments reported by Mendel in 1865 and the discovery of the chromosome arrangement of genes in the early 20th century. But the real age of the new biology began in 1952 and continues to this day.

1952	J. D. Watson, F. M. C. Crick and associates discover the double helical structure of DNA (deoxyribonucleicacid) molecule —one of the two basic chemicals involved in the genetic language.
1956	A. Kornberg discovers the enzyme catalyst which leads to the transfer (copying) of genetic information.
1961	M. W. Nirenberg begins to decipher the genetic code.
1966	R. W. Holley and M. G. Khorana complete the deciphering.
1966-67	S. Spiegelman, and A. Kornberg and associates use enzymes to copy DNA from a virus — thus achieving the 'replication of Life.'

THE LASER

In 7 years the Light Amplification Through Stimulated Emission of Radiation (LASER) became an important practical scientific discovery. The LASER has been used for such varied applications as drilling strong metals and delicate eye surgery.

1958	Extension of MASER principle for experiments in LASER theory.
1960	Building of operational LASER.
1961	Continuous operating gas LASER.
1961	Experiments in high speed optical computers.
1963	Experimental LASER use in satellite tracking.
1963	Eye surgery using LASERS.
1965	Widespread commercial work in medical, scientific and industrial LASER applications.

MAN AND THE COMPUTER

MAN
AND THE
COMPUTER

Technology as an
Agent of Social Change

JOHN DIEBOLD

FREDERICK A. PRAEGER, *Publishers*
New York · Washington · London

FREDERICK A. PRAEGER, *Publishers*
111 Fourth Avenue, New York, N.Y. 10003, U.S.A.
5, Cromwell Place, London S.W.7, England

Published in the United States of America in 1969
by Frederick A. Praeger, Inc., Publishers

© 1969 by Frederick A. Praeger, Inc.

All rights reserved

Library of Congress Catalog Card Number: 70–75237

Printed in the United States of America

For Joan, who will live in
the world emerging from today's change

PREFACE

What has always made machines truly important to man is not their individual versatility and productivity—it is the fact that they serve as agents of social change. They change our world. They change us. This is the theme of the present book.

It is an inescapable fact of our times that science and technology are changing our world—changing it beyond anything we may imagine or desire. Too often, our view of this change is shortsighted. It occurs after the fact, and it assigns too small a role to the future.

This is not a book of prophecy; yet, as I review its plan, I find that it inevitably contains elements that could be interpreted as dire, for its essence is the impact of science and technology on *Man*. Thus, while my thoughts are questioning rather than apocalyptic, and I am trying to put them into language that is direct rather than portentous, I am still haunted by the words of Richard Wilbur, who wrote not long ago a poem entitled "Advice to a Prophet":

> When you come, as soon you must, to the streets of our city,
> Mad-eyed from stating the obvious,
> Not proclaiming our fall but begging us
> In God's name to have self-pity.
>
> Spare us all word of the weapons, their force and range,
> The long numbers that rocket the mind;
> Our slow, unreckoning hearts will be left behind,
> Unable to fear what is too strange.

Nor shall you scare us with talk of the death of the race.
How should we dream of this place without us?
The sun mere fire, the leaves untroubled about us,
A stone look on the stone's face?

Speak of the world's own change. . . .*

It is the purpose here to present the "world's own change," briefly and by direct example. The plan was first to explore the setting and a few of the more immediate examples of change. Next, three specific cases are discussed in some detail. Finally, a number of long-term questions are raised.

The thoughts developed in this book have evolved over a number of years, and I have expressed them, in whole or in part, on various occasions. Each chapter is, therefore, preceded by one or more attributions to speeches or other documents in which I first expressed these thoughts in the form here presented. Of course, a considerable amount of updating and editing has gone into this book, but the original dates of the material on which it is based may be of some interest to the reader.

Chapter 1, "The Profound Impact of Science and Technology," is based on a February, 1966, address before an Economic Club of Chicago dinner meeting.

Chapter 2, "Educational Technology and Business Responsibility," is based on an October, 1966, Alumni Day dinner address at Swarthmore College.

Chapter 3, "International Disparities," is based on an

* © 1959 by Richard Wilbur. Reprinted from his volume *Advice to a Prophet and Other Poems* by permission of Harcourt, Brace & World, Inc.

article originally published in the January, 1968, issue of *Foreign Affairs,* the quarterly journal of The Council on Foreign Relations.

Chapter 4, "The Training of Managers," is based on a February, 1965, address presented upon the occasion of receipt of an honorary doctor-of-science degree at a special convocation of the Clarkson College of Technology.

Chapter 5, "The Long-Term Questions," is based on a February, 1965, address presented upon the occasion of receipt of an honorary doctor-of-laws degree at a Founder's Day convocation of Rollins College.

Herbert J. Blitz, Executive Secretary of The Diebold Institute for Public Policy Studies, edited, updated, rearranged, polished, and argued and made this book a reality. And Miriam Z. Klipper did what only the best editors of the best publishers can do: She was merciless in her criticisms and charming in presenting them. Many friends and associates have contributed their ideas and expert knowledge. The list of names includes men from business (including members of my own firm) and from the universities. I am grateful to them all but have confined myself here to acknowledging those who have contributed directly to the work on this book, the consummation of the other efforts.

JOHN DIEBOLD

New York, New York
February, 1969

CONTENTS

MAN AND THE COMPUTER

Chapter 1

THE PROFOUND IMPACT
OF SCIENCE AND TECHNOLOGY

*Scientific and technological advances present
mankind with immediate and profound
questions. The importance of machines and
innovations resides in the impact they have
on human beings—in their roles as agents
for social change. They affect not only the
means but also the ends of individual and
societal actions.*

*Our age is characterized by the accelerating
rapidity of scientifically and technologically
based changes, particularly those brought
about by advances in computer and communications technologies. Information is at
the heart of society, and its use profoundly
affects this and future generations. Individuals and institutions are being put under
enormous pressures, and we must seek to
identify the causes and the directions of*

*these pressures. Then we can hope to alter
our institutions to meet the needs of man in
a time of rapid and fundamental change.*

*This chapter is based on an address at a dinner meeting
of the Economic Club of Chicago.*

The new movement in science and technology, centered on new and rapidly expanding information processing and communications capabilities, is often described as a "revolution." This word is much over-used. There seems to be a political revolution somewhere in the world at least once a month; and every time a new playpen is put on the market, the manufacturer announces it as revolutionary. A sign seen recently in a Third Avenue bakery said, "Revolutionary new old-fashioned donuts"!

But when the past two or three decades of scientific and technological discovery are called a "revolution," I believe the word is used in the same sense as when the phrase Industrial Revolution is applied to the great upheaval based on technical advance that started two centuries ago. That revolution brought about significant social, political, and economic changes, which is what the latest scientific and technological discoveries are doing now.

The Industrial Revolution was called a "revolution" because it created a new environment for mankind, a new way of life. What it gave to history was much more than the steam engine and the cotton gin, the railway and the power loom: it gave society a new tempo, a new outlook. It took men off the fields and out of small shops and, for the first time, put them into factory life. Hence it gave us mass production and, through mass production, the first civilization in history in which luxury was not confined to a few. It gave us as well a sense of hurry, of time, that is still unknown in countries that have not gone through an industrial revolution. It gave us a sense of material progress, an itch to get ahead that is also unknown in the parts of the world that are still pre-industrial. In other words, the machines the Industrial Revolution produced were agents for enormous social change. No one, least of all Richard Arkwright or James Watt, thought that he was changing civilization itself. Yet, for us, looking back, that is precisely what was *revolutionary* about the inventions they made.

The current technological revolution promises to have far wider effects than the merely technological. Like James Watt and Richard Arkwright, many of our present-day inventors have no intention of reshaping our entire world. Yet that is what they are doing. Today, we are dealing with machines that can change society much more rapidly and profoundly than the machines that accompanied the "Industrial Revolution" of the late eighteenth and nineteenth centuries because they deal with the stuff of which society is made—information and its communication.

Leisure is a good example of the extent of the change. We talk a great deal about leisure, but we don't know what leisure will be like in the future. A hundred years ago, when it was necessary for most people to work sixty or seventy hours a week in miserable factories in order to survive, the question of what to do with nonwork—with leisure—never presented itself. Today with most people having forty hours or less of work each week, leisure time is already beginning to have a profound effect on our lives and economy.

Yet, new demands on individuals for their time are constantly increasing. There will be much work to do in the future—work on things we cannot even afford to contemplate doing today. This work will involve raising the quality of our lives—educationally, culturally, and in terms of human relations—in a wide range of personalized activities such as teaching, legal aid, policy work, health care, and counseling. It would enlist individuals in taking responsibility for the total environment. Will this be "leisure" work? Will our earnings expectations continue to rise, and will we be paid for this kind of work? Who will pay? How will our social and economic structure require readaptation?

We should be raising basic questions as to whether we learn in order to earn a living or learn to live and who will teach us. Technology is intimately related to human and social problems. To what extent will computer-programed education be effective and socially desirable? Major questions already are being raised on this subject. We are experimenting with the chemical stimulation of learning processes, and with genetic changes in this regard. Vannevar Bush points to the probability of man-machine symbiosis—the linking of a man's brain directly into the memory and calculating power of electronic computers. He envisages gigantic machine memories accessible to our minds—providing something akin to Jung's collective unconscious by making available all human knowledge and experience to the memory of every individual. Are we threatened with intellectual overdevelopment in relation to our emotional capacities? Are we heading into a time when Dr. Faustus becomes Everyman?

Scientific and technological advances will take us beyond the civilization of an industrial society and will raise an entirely new set of social, economic, and business problems. They will tax our ingenuity to its utmost.

The fruits of science lengthen our life and throughout that life decrease the toll of sickness and disease. Yet this precious gift in itself poses such an awesome burden of population that for the great bulk of individuals alive today—those who do not know whether the substance to sustain life tomorrow will be forthcoming today—the agony of living is made acute.

The chemical magic that pours forth from our laboratories and process plants and kills insects, preserves crops from blight, and promotes cleanliness unknown before detergents also turns out to be a not-unalloyed blessing, for it brings the specter of Rachel Carson's silent spring.

The harnessed power of the automobile brings the open countryside within an afternoon's reach to city dwellers who would otherwise never see trees; it brings patients within reach of emergency medical treatment; it changes for the better much of our life, but it too is accompanied by congestion, by the blight of highways, and by the pollution of the air we breathe.

Automation produces changes in the skill requirements of our workers, and when it comes at the time of economic problems, it can confront us with the paradoxical situation of unemployment and shortages of skilled manpower.

Information technology is leading us to the construction of machines that exhibit most of what we have previously meant by "intelligence"—machines that can truly be said to learn and machines that not only respond intelligently to spoken commands but also speak. That such machines will pose problems as well as opportunity is already evident. Some of the problems will be as fundamental as man's questioning his role in the world.

The cornucopia of the life sciences has only begun to overflow. We know that among the gifts that pour forth will be an ability to unlock and soon to change the genetic code, thus giving us the awesome, frightening means for changing the form of future generations of mankind.

These are just a few examples of the problems already confronting us as individuals and as a society. But perhaps the one phenomenon most characteristic of our age is the rate of change itself.

THE RATE AND PATTERN OF CHANGE

The technological advances that sparked the current revolution were the result of military research at the end of World War II, but advances continued at an accelerating rate through the succeeding years and have sustained the original inspiration in what appears to be an endless succession of inventions. Half of the scientific research conducted in United States since the Republic was founded has been crowded into the last eight years; 90 per cent of all the scientists who have ever lived in the history of mankind are alive today.

Research has unprecedented financial support. At the beginning of 1940, in the United States a total of $280 million a year was being spent on all the research and development. Now the figure is $25 billion, and by 1975 the rate may well be in the neighborhood of $40 billion annually. Thus, an increase from $280 million to $40 billion in thirty-five years is projected, and there is no sign that the rate of innovation and invention will diminish. Each new invention brings with it a revision of our estimates of the future.

It is possible to identify the crucial elements in this innovative process and to apprehend the underlying pattern that determines its impact on the rate of change.

The Uses of the Computer

At the heart of the current scientific and technological revolution is the newly found ability to build information systems. Late in the 1940's, credence was given to the forecast that a dozen high speed computers would be able to handle all the calculations required in the United States. Today, more than fifty thousand computers are installed in this country, and by 1972 this figure is expected to exceed one hundred thousand.

The computer industry is entirely new; yet its output already is at $6.3 billion annually and by 1972 will have grown to almost $9.0 billion. By the turn of the decade, investment in computers and related equipment will exceed 10 per cent of total U.S. private investment in new plant and machinery. This alone indicates that the computer industry, while still in its childhood, has become a central factor in the operations of our economy.

Indeed, the computer is a part of everyday life for nearly all of us, whether we are conscious of it or not. It processes our tax records and allows insurance adjusters to make prompt settlements. It provides an engineer with prompt evaluations of the many alternatives in designing an airplane wing, giving us safer and faster airplanes. The computer allows the businessman to operate his plant efficiently, the labor union to perform complex calculations of cost and relative value of alternative fringe benefits while contracts are being negotiated, the government administrator to keep track of 60 million Social Security records, the police to know which drivers have not paid their parking fines, the politician to determine how to spend his time and money in election campaigns, and the religious scholar to catalogue the Dead Sea Scrolls in proper sequence. These are, of course, impressive uses of computer technology, but they are only ways of speeding up or improving what we have been doing all along. Until now, we have been using computers mostly to sort out the chaos that fantastic growth has confronted us with—a growth actually made possible, economically and mechanically, however, by the computers themselves.

The computer industry is rapidly changing. Up to 1945, when the first electronic computer was built, man's calculating speed for several thousand years had been the speed of the abacus. Overnight, it increased five times. From 1945 to 1951, it increased one hundred times again, and, from then until now, it has increased one thousand times again. Our measure of calculations today is nanoseconds—one-billionth of a second. A nanosecond has the same relationship to a second that a second has to thirty years. This scale of speed is very hard to comprehend, but even this speed is too slow for the complex problems that computers are now being asked to solve. The distance that an electron has to move from one part of a circuit to another part has become a major limitation on the speed at which a computer works and a major challenge to the people designing computers. One of the main reasons for producing smaller and smaller components is to get the pieces closer together so that the electrons will not have to go so far, since they travel at the relatively slow speed of somewhat less than 186,000 miles a second!

We completely lack a frame of reference that allows us to envisage the vast scale of change inherent in these developments in information technology and its widespread applications. Not only is man's productivity being increased, but our experience of life is being affected by the new machines. Today's machines are a far more powerful agent for social change than were those of the first Industrial Revolution. With these machines, we are building systems that translate (still crudely) from one language to another, respond to the human voice, devise their own routes to goals that are presented to them, and improve their performance as a result of encountering the environment—systems that "learn" in the sense in which the term is usually used. These are machine systems that deal with the very core of human society—with information, its communication, and use. They represent developments that augur far more for mankind than just net changes in manpower, more or less employment, and new ways of doing old tasks.

Because of these systems, mankind will undertake new tasks, not merely perform old tasks in a new way. The same technology that enables us to build machines that translate, although primitively, Russian documents into English has already given us a laboratory version of a machine that translates the spoken word from one language to another. Hospital records are now being maintained automatically, and the same machines are starting to be used by physicians to help in diagnosis and to pick trends from thousands of medical records to assist in truly preventive medicine. A newspaper that today uses a computer in preparing paper tape to automatically set type will tomorrow use a machine that transmits a television image of the newspaper page on the editor's desk directly to the printing press. The day after tomorrow, we will have the means to print material out of the television set in our living room.

Today's newspapers will not be printed out of the television set, and today's publishers will not be offering the service. A key characteristic of the new technology is that it will allow the housewife at home, the physician at his office, the engineer or scientist at his laboratory, the businessman at his desk great selectivity to ask for specific information that is of interest to him and to receive answers to such inquiries virtually as he makes them, whether they be book reviews, the results of a baseball game, an intricate problem involving pharmaceutical research or financial analysis. Editorial work is going to be changed. Instead of the static process of providing the reader with what we *think* he wants or needs, the use of these systems is going to allow dialogue with the system itself.

There are already services that allow an employer to request of a computer—often hundreds or several thousands of miles away—résumés of potential professional employees. There is thus a job exchange that could do much to insure, on a wide basis, the matching of unemployed people with job openings over large areas. Thus, technology will be able to smooth over employment difficulties.

The same principles that lie at the heart of the new and amusing businesses in which computers select blind dates are already being applied to the matching of apartment and house availabilities with people's needs and desires in the real estate market. Today's computer-inspired novelties are going to change totally the way in which much business and professional work is conducted by the mid-1970's. By the late 1970's and early 1980's, the decreasing costs and improved capabilities of this technology will allow the communications center of the home to be a reality.

The Growth of New Industries

The areas of computer-based and communications-based capabilities will be brought into existence by, and will create the demand for, major new industries. The first major entrepreneurial opportunity is the industry that supplies the systems and the equipment; this is already a several billion dollar industry. The second new industry is the about-to-bloom data utility industry, analogous in some ways to the electric utility industry. A large central processor handles information at a very low unit cost, just as a large central generator produces electricity for many customers at a low unit cost. It is cheaper for many people to make use of this central utility than it is for each individual to have his own generator. The same economic reasoning applies to the data utility industry, where many people can use the machine simultaneously because of the technologies of real-time processing, time-sharing, and communication. Small and medium-sized businesses and, for some purposes, large businesses will just plug in for data as we now do for electricity. An interesting question is which business institutions are going to be the suppliers for this industry. Banks are especially well positioned to capitalize on it. Will they take a fresh view of their own business service and fundamental nature in order to do so?

A third new industry is the one now being called the inquiry industry; in some ways it is the publishing field of the future. Its development allows the sale of proprietary data over a communication system in answer to a query placed by the customer from a unit on his desk. For instance, it is the kind of system where you could ask for a selection of stocks, classified by price/earnings ratios. You key this request into the unit on your desk, see the answer on the screen nearly as soon as you ask the question, and then ask another question and so on through a series of questions. When you get what you want, you can even make a copy of it if you so desire. When such systems are in use, we shall be able to speak of an information explosion, for then there will be an exponential increase in the use of information. The licensing agreement between IBM and Dun & Bradstreet is a step in the direction of this type of development. Some electronic corporations have purchased publishing companies. This is just the beginning; there will be major changes in ownership in this area in the near future as businesses begin to position themselves to sell proprietary data.

A fourth example is an industry of computer-based educational systems. As technology allows a dynamic relationship between a student and a machine system that answers questions as they are posed and can discern gaps in a student's basic grasp of a subject, the much heralded but until now disappointing teaching machines (it would be better if they were called learning machines) will begin to be more effective than they generally are. Such systems are already at work in some industrial situations; IBM's maintenance training is a good example. Another is the use by mentally handicapped children, of computer-driven typewriters, which have been able to overcome some of their handicaps. A number of other experimental programs have also been initiated, and they will be discussed in Chapter 2. Up to now, some twenty thousand children have received as much as half an hour of computer-assisted instruction daily in various locations throughout the United States. It appears highly probable that, through this technology of learning systems, the entire world of education can be changed. Today, the costs for such systems are prohibitive for widespread individual use. However, this may not be true for very long, and, when parents find that children using them learn more rapidly than those who do not, they will demand such systems because of their effectiveness.

There are other examples of emerging new industries that could be mentioned. The rate of change that result from this technology manifests itself in the new ways we conduct our lives, in the processes that are able to support a vastly expanding number and variety of activities, and in the creation of new industries.

The Continuum of Discovery

The versatility of the new information and communications technologies makes possible scientific and technological advances undreamt of even thirty years ago. Calculations that would have required decades of man-hours now can be done in minutes. Pertinent information that would have been buried in libraries and laboratories scattered throughout the world can be found and applied with increasing effectiveness to the work of scientists and technicians. We have taken a quantum jump in the creation of new knowledge, which is, in turn, applied to the solution of new problems and the raising of new questions.

Until now, this process has been confined mainly to the achievement of scientific and technological advances, which, while in many ways benefiting man, threaten social and environmental consequences for which he is unprepared.

INDIVIDUAL AND INSTITUTIONAL IMPACT
Manpower, Finance, and Planning

To begin, there is the matter of unemployment brought about by automation, which is probably relatively susceptible to the simplest and most direct solutions. Mass unemployment, even a fairly high rate of unemployment is not inevitable.

There is no doubt that technological advances have made, and are continuing to make, changes in the content and purpose of all types of jobs. To take a simple example: a steelworker who formerly tested the molten ore and then told workmen to proceed with the next step of the operation now monitors a control panel that activates machinery that will move the metal to the next phase of the process. Not only is the operation speeded up, but fewer workmen are needed on the job. A crucial question is raised: What will the redundant steelworkers do?

Some of the major unfulfilled demands of our society are in transportation and housing. There is also a need for more and different schools, for new means to provide police protection, sanitation, water, and air pollution control. The response to these demands will provide jobs—directly and indirectly—for the redundant steelworkers. These same individuals may not fill the new jobs created, but there can be a redeployment of labor, so that, after suitable retraining, a worker from a steel plant can move into a job vacated or not taken by a worker who is filling one of the new jobs. There will be no lack of demand for manpower.

Of course, the transitions cannot be made simply. There will have to be a shift in political and economic priorities. Capital is needed to meet the transportation, housing and other demands. It has become evident that, as U.S. business investment is increasingly applied to the modernization of equipment and facilities, the productivity of capital simultaneously is increasing. This means not only that less labor is required per unit of output but also less capital. There comes a point at which it will be profitable to invest elsewhere the capital no longer needed for the production of goods that today take most of our investment expenditures.

The government can encourage business to invest in such areas as transportation, housing, and education by offering incentives—tax deductions, guaranteed joint ventures, contracts, and so forth. For instance, a start has already been made in California, where aerospace firms have contracted with the state government to seek new approaches to such matters as air and water pollution, transportation, and crime control. Much more will be happening along these lines.

There is need for a relatively mobile labor force and appropriate training and retraining programs backed by both management and labor. There must be fundamental changes in our educational methods to enable students to learn how to learn instead of only acquiring specific skills that are subject to obsolescence. Organized labor—if it is to regain the vital place it once held in our society—will have to actively pursue programs designed to teach its membership new skills. And both management and labor will have to learn to come to agreements on pension rights and on their specific areas of responsibility so as to allow for greater labor mobility.

All these points are linked to the need for planning. The changes occurring in our society can be harmful if not anticipated and planned for. The needs of society must be planned for. Private capital must be involved in coping with specific areas. Labor must work with capital to minimize individual hardships and to increase individual opportunity. To plan successively, however, the range and the depth of the technological revolution must be understood.

Technological change has always been a temporary threat to the worker and to the businessman. Consider what the automobile did to the harness-maker and the blacksmith. Indeed, we survived such changes without planning, and sometimes it appears that we didn't give them a second thought. What is so different today? The answer is that our attitudes have changed. A major reason for our present concern with technological unemployment is the fact that we now have higher standards with respect to society's obligations to the individual. We, as a society, are not content to watch a worker and a family struggle unaided against the forces of change. Nor should we be. And we are no longer isolated from other countries, that are not only applying the technology we in the United States develop but are aggressively developing science and technology themselves. The applications of technology abroad affect employment in this country. The worst thing for American labor would be a slackening in the application of science and technology in our country. We could quickly find ourselves at a considerable competitive disadvantage in domestic and foreign markets and could be faced with unemployment with no chance of redeployment in a depressed economy.

The Continuum of Social Impact

The most fundamental questions posed by science and technology are moral, spiritual, legal, ethical, and political, and these questions should concern us far more than do the obvious and rather easily soluble problems of manpower and employment. When we have the means to record and retrieve a record of all one's actions, who will exercise self-restraint in its use and misuse? As we come to possess the power to control human behavior, who will make the decisions about how it is to be used? When we can determine the physical appearance and mental makeup of future generations, who will decide if a child is to be brilliant or beautiful or both?

Insofar as we must begin now to plan for the consequences of science and technology, they represent challenges of the most immediate nature. The threat to individual privacy, the power to control human behavior, and the ability to affect genetic development may face us at different times over the next three decades. The first two of these are close upon us, and the third may not reveal itself fully until the end of the century. But they partake in large measure of the same order of things: the problem of individual man inadequately protected by social institutions, laws, and precepts formulated by his forbears to meet different challenges. Therefore, it is useful to complete this introductory survey with a look at the institutional framework of our society and its responsiveness to the changes that are upon us.

Institutions

It would appear that most labor unions, as social institutions, are still dominated by the experience of the Depression years, the 1930's, when they first became a great power in this country. Their philosophy and leadership are geared to the economic and social environment that existed then. For instance, the traditional craft structure daily becomes less appropriate to the world that science is building. The specialization that developed around earlier tools and machines is not going to be effective in the computer age, and unions must realize this and change their structures and goals. The problem of training for new skills is going to be with us for a long time, and it is here that the unions can and must play an important role. The reappraisal must go even further, for not only collective bargaining but the problem of the role of unions, of the rights of public employees, and of pension funds and employment security, must be looked at in the context of changing demands for workers in different areas of production and service. Neither society nor the workers directly involved are helped by featherbedding and artificial obstacles to new house-building or newspaper printing or cargo-handling. The means of economic production are changing, the product itself is changing at an accelerating rate, but our labor-management concepts remain unchanged.

Science has not only provided the businessman with new ways of producing traditional products but it provides new products that we have scarcely begun to appreciate on a wide scale. The technological revolution is materially changing what the businessman does as well as how he does it. The immediate impact of automation usually consists in improving the methods by which work is done by the introduction of new machinery and new procedures. Less obvious, but just as fundamental, are the changes in what is done. The telephone company, for example, finds that machines rather than people are becoming the largest user of long lines. New products and services create new demands. Altering economic and environmental conditions creates new needs to be filled and signifies a major change in the way of doing business. The world of business is changing—the way managers manage and also what they manage.

One of the key areas of concern is the use of new approaches to bring the financial, managerial, and technological resources of the private sector into the over-all process of accommodating our society to the qualitative changes in life. Of course, inroads have already been made in the rehabilitation of the cities, in transportation, in municipal government. But in comparison to the resources we need and which the private sector—including foundations, universities, and labor unions—still has available to it, the surface has hardly been broken. If the private sector is not imaginative enough to use its resources—actually to sell itself, its resources, and services —for this job, then government will do it. To do so, it will have to appropriate the resources of the private sector. This is not a pleasant prospect, either in terms of our traditions of diversity and freedom or in terms of getting the job done well.

Government officials find that their world, too, is changing enormously as a result of technology. At a White House conference in 1962, President Kennedy said:

> The fact of the matter is that most of the problems or at least many of them that we now face are technical problems, are administrative problems. They are very sophisticated judgments which do not lend themselves to the great sort of passionate movements which have stirred this country so often in the past. Now they deal with questions which are beyond the comprehension of most men, most governmental administrators, over which experts may differ.

Government structures in their present forms can no longer deal with the mounting pressures on them. Examples are state, municipal, and county governments and school systems. New approaches to their financing and functional relationships to society and to each other must be found. New institutions must be built and others replaced or abolished. Just three of the many problems already upon us that require major institutional change if our society is to benefit from and not be stifled by technology range from the safe landing of supersonic aircraft to the effective prevention of technologically sophisticated criminal activities to the provision of serviceable modern ground transportation. The problems faced by our government institutions are indeed awesome. They boil down to the necessity of creating an environment conducive and adaptable to rapid change. Every element in our society must be alerted to the mutations and permutations engendered by technological advances, in order that we may gain and not lose because of them.

QUESTIONS

Almost all the forces affecting our various institutions are becoming increasingly interdependent, as are the scientific and technological disciplines themselves. Thus, computer technology in its most advanced forms is becoming dependent on an understanding of biological processes. Racial violence in Watts appeared to be related to inadequate transportation facilities. The air in Manhattan is affected by industrial development policies in New Jersey and by the competitive structure of the automobile industry. Legal safeguards will affect the application of scientific discoveries to educational methods, but that should not prevent us from trying to organize problem areas and approaches. We must start somewhere. Once some movement in grappling with the substantive questions has been achieved, organizational emphasis can be changed.

The practical way in which the challenges of this new age can be met is by insuring that major social innovations will accompany each technological innovation. This book centers around three fundamental questions: (1) What are the major social problems and opportunities that flow from rapid advances in science and technology? (2) How do we plan to meet these problems and exploit these opportunities? (3) What goals are we going to set for ourselves?

It is not clear how much time we have to answer these questions, but the first priority is to ask them. Technology cannot do that for us. We face a world in which one thing is certain: fundamental change. We are leaving the push-button age. Today the buttons push themselves.

Chapter 2

EDUCATIONAL TECHNOLOGY
AND BUSINESS RESPONSIBILITY

As the first of three case studies showing technology as an agent of social change, the interaction of education and technology is presented here. While education makes technological advances possible, this very achievement places education under new stresses that require institutional and methodological changes. What we must learn is rapidly changing. Therefore, the way we learn must change as well, and integral to the response of the educational system is the use of technology itself.

The business sector is capable of making a major contribution to this response; it can serve a market of immense potential. In order to do so, it must assume an appropriate share of the responsibilities for the educational process. Business must ask, and seek answers to, the fundamental questions of ed-

ucation. The business response demonstrates the problems inherent in new technologies, which produce new markets and necessitate genuine innovations within the institutions of business. Here is a precursor of future challenges and opportunities. One of its most interesting aspects is that business, in meeting its own internal educational and training problems, is likely to lead the way in the application of advanced technologies for our educational institutions.

This chapter is based on an Alumni Day dinner address given at Swarthmore College, Swarthmore, Pa.

INTRODUCTION

The interaction between technology and society, between machine and man, is nowhere more profound than in the education of society and man. Technology changes the need for education, develops from education, and can serve education. There is no doubt whatever that computer, communications, and biochemical technologies are going to help bring about the first really important change in the learning process. Movable type, for example, widened the impact of learning—brought it to those who had previously considered their past and present environment from hearing story-tellers and balladeers—but it did not change the process itself. This fundamental change is what today's innovations are directly concerned with. The question is: how and when will new learning processes be applied?

The impact of educational technology on business, at least in the United States, is going to be phenomenal. It will change not only the markets business serves but also the operation of business. It is becoming evident that the first applications of technology to the educational process will in all probability start within businesses. The fact that in business students are paid salaries while learning and the application of new methods is not constrained by an educational "establishment" encourages the early introduction of techniques that have demonstrated cost-performance improvements over other, older, methods. But can and will business transfer its accumulating experience to the responsible service of the much larger general educational market?

There is another and even more striking aspect of the

relationship between business and educational technology. This relationship is actually a case study of the future—an example of technology producing new markets but requiring, in order to reach these markets, genuine innovations within the institutions of business. It is representative of the peculiarly complex processes of innovation—technological, methodological, philosophical—through which private enterprise must expand its roles and responsibilities in our emerging post-industrial civilization. This case study of the technological impact on business is best developed within the wider context of the social forces acting to bring about the introduction of educational technologies. To do this, three major related strands of interaction between technology and the educational process will be examined:

• *Technologically caused social forces making for educational change.* These consist of population pressures, a vast expansion in the production of and need for information, the increasing rate of environmental changes, and the growing aspirations of the less developed countries.

• *Response to these forces in education as it involves educational institutions, systems, and technologies.* Contradictory currents are at work here: desire for and resistance to change, recognition of the need for innovation and inadequate knowledge of how to bring it about and of its consequences.

• *Response of business to the resultant realities and responsibilities of the educational market.* Here again there are sharp differences: initial over-optimism followed by profound disappointment and defeatism. Yet a body of careful analysis is beginning to grow over the rubble of the past and a major breakthrough may be possible sooner than the skeptics, once severely burned, have the courage to admit publicly.

What this chapter attempts is a severe and not always encouraging examination of some of the educational questions facing society. Right now we can be sure of only three things—and all three of them can be stated in terms of potential dangers. The first has been described by Alfred North Whitehead:

> In the conditions of modern life the rule is absolute, the race which does not value trained intelligence is doomed. Not all your heroism, not all your social charm, not all your wit, not all your victories on land or at sea, can move back the finger of fate. Today we maintain ourselves. Tomorrow science will have moved forward yet one more step; and there will be no appeal from the judgment which will then be pronounced on the uneducated.

The second danger is that technology could be applied to education in ways that may change societies and individuals to their detriment. Henry Adams wrote: "The chief wonder of education is that it does not ruin everybody concerned with it, teachers and taught." The complex and relatively unassessed forces of technology, as they may be applied to the learning process, escalate those words from a witty aphorism to an unpleasant threat.

The third danger is that technology may not be applied soon enough to education to avert the first danger or wisely enough to avert the second. It has been stated that it takes forty years for innovations to be implemented in education. The danger we face is illustrated by two quotations, which can be read almost in parallel:

> Various methods of individual instruction have been adopted in recent years. . . . In lower schools differentiated curricula . . . have been arranged. Experiments have also been tried with minimum assignments for the abler pupils. Sometimes pupils have been classified according to ability, and instruction has been adapted by various devices to the different classes.
>
> Individual teaching is sometimes carried a step farther. Each pupil is thought of as so distinctly different from all other pupils that he is allowed to exercise his initiative not only with regard to methods of study but with regard to the topics to be studied. Class organization and the coherent sequences which have characterized the traditional courses of instruction are sometimes abandoned and the individual is encouraged to discover and follow his personal intellectual or practical interests.

> We can envision the time of universal individualized education, when every person will be educated and no two will be educated alike, when teachers deeply committed to the art of teaching and thoroughly versed in the science of learning will have at their disposal a full panoply of learning materials to which they will direct each individual student in accordance with his needs, abilities and interests. There will be no lockstep and no common schedule. Each student will proceed at his own pace through a curriculum uniquely adjusted to his needs. . . . He will move smoothly and early from directed, highly structured learning situations to self-directed unprestructured activities, where he as a learner plays an active role in learning.

The first quotation is taken from the report of the President's Research Committee on Social Trends, which has a foreword by former President Herbert Hoover, dated October 11, 1932. The second quotation is from an article by Norman D. Kurland, in the October 30, 1968, issue of *Educational Technology*. Are the forty years up, or are they just beginning?

These then are the major strands of interaction between technology and education and some of the major questions arising from this interaction. A detailed examination of them reveals enormous opportunities for society and for private enterprise serving society. It also reveals conflicts and dangers. On the basis of such an examination, this chapter concludes with a number of suggestions regarding the response of governmental, educational, and business institutions.

FORCES MAKING FOR EDUCATIONAL CHANGE

Unprecedented demands are made on our educational system. The nature of these pressures and of the forces underlying them takes out of our hands the option of whether we wish to make basic changes in our educational structure and methods. It leaves only the question of what form the changes will take. The longer we wait in formulating a response, the less the range of our choice and the greater the problem.

Population Explosion

The pressures resulting from the population explosion are already so familiar to all of us that they will not be dwelled upon except to restate briefly the most fundamental statistics. In the fifty years between 1910 and 1960, the population of the United States nearly doubled. The rate of increase itself is increasing. In the decade between

1957 and 1967, the population jumped approximately 25 million, from 175 million to 200 million. By 1977, a U.S. population of 230 million is predicted. But, as will be seen later in this chapter, educational needs are determined not only by population statistics but also by the length of time and the number of times people must be educated and re-educated.

Perhaps most immediately relevant of all are the forces that make up the dilemma of our poor; 20 per cent of our population is being pulled into the gutters of alienation and self-hatred by the vacuum left behind the onrush of technological change. While the ghettos grow, the opportunities for their inhabitants, determined by their education, vanish in the wake of technological progress. For example, 44 per cent of the current job vacancies in New York City are for white-collar jobs. Only 13 per cent of the unemployed in the three major ghetto areas of New York City—Harlem, East Harlem, and Bedford-Stuyvesant—have ever had a white-collar job at any time. A person with less than an eighth grade education is simply not equipped to cope adequately with problems in the world today. Yet there are estimated to be 25 million adults—eighteen years of age or over—in the United States with less than an eighth-grade education. In ten years, it is predicted, only 4 per cent of the employment market will be open to the unskilled.

Information Explosion

The information explosion is even more dramatic than the population explosion. Increasing at an exponential rate are the sheer mass and complexity of information produced by today's activities and necessary in varying degrees to the conduct of today's life and, thus, a further demand on the educational process. There is more and more to learn about every aspect of our work and the world about us.

To a certain extent, this problem has been dealt with by increasing specialization in the most advanced fields of knowledge. But the use of this expedient has been accompanied by greater awareness of its limitations. Will Rogers summed up the matter when he said: "There is nothing more stupid than an educated man, if you get off the thing he was educated in." C. P. Snow more recently has discussed it in terms of two cultures, the humanistic and scientific, whose members find it difficult to communicate with each other.

Probably most serious is the problem of teaching the vast majority of people enough to enable them to participate meaningfully in society. This is not a problem only of the underprivileged; it has made itself felt in the anti-intellectualism of college demonstrators as well.

The amount of information produced is estimated to double every ten years. But the most advanced and difficult-to-acquire portions of this information have a 50 per cent obsolescence rate over the same period. At the same time, 90 per cent of all the scientists in the history of the world are alive and working today. They face the most acute crises of information availability and obsolescence. Research is constantly producing with fierce rapidity wholly new fields of knowledge, professional disciplines, and occupations. Yet it is a reflection of the human toll of our inability to respond adequately to this force of change that many of the terms used to name and describe the new jobs becoming available have little or no meaning to a large part of the population seeking and needing employment.

Increasing Rate of Environmental Change

Accelerating environmental change is relatively new in the scope and penetration of its effect. Although in large part a result of the two forces of change already mentioned, it represents a distinct and important phenomenon of its own.

No better description of the past condition of mankind can be found than in Robert L. Heilbroner's book *The Future as History:*

> That condition was mankind's stasis, its changelessness, its inertness. To be sure, the immediate pageant of what we usually call "history" was marked with all its triumphs and tragedies, its turns and twists; while from our now remote vantage point we can discern the rise and fall of larger tides of cultures and civilizations. But from the point of view of the anonymous millions who constituted those societies, neither the pageants nor the tides were such that daily life could be reliably harnessed to them. . . . It is but a slight error, if error it be at all, to picture the life horizons of the overwhelming majority of men in fifteenth century Europe as essentially unchanged from what they had been in the fifth century B.C. Greece, or the experience of existence for the Asian cultivator of 1900 as in no significant way elevated over that of his remote forebears two thousand years before. Certainly whatever elevation there had been was to be measured not by generations, but by centuries.

There remain small pockets in this world where this may still be so, but even in those places the transistor radio is becoming a central fact of life. In America, we have gone in three generations from a rural to an urban society, in two generations from being an isolated giant standing aloof in one corner of the earth to an omnipresent world leader and arbiter, in one generation from train to jet to space travel. There are with us today men in their fifties and sixties who confidently expected to have learned enough in their teens to last them through a life of work and leisure. Few who are in their teens in the final third of the twentieth century have learned enough to see them successfully into the next decade, let alone into retirement.

The Aspirations of the Less-Developed Countries

The newly awakened aspirations of the bulk of mankind that lives today not knowing if tomorrow's food will be forthcoming constitute a demand of unparalleled magnitude on the world's educational system. If we have difficulty comprehending the magnitude of the information explosion, we lack altogether a frame of reference that will allow our imagination to encompass the scale of the educational problem posed by this human awakening. Statistics barely begin to paint the picture. In Argentina, a relatively advanced nation, for example, out of a total population of some 21 million, less than 3 million receive primary education, less than 600,000 secondary education, and less than 200,000 are enrolled in colleges or universities. In Ethiopia, a country of the same population size, only 250,000 receive primary, 12,000 receive secondary, and 1,000 receive higher education. In some of the emerging African nations, national education systems are nonexistent. There were sixteen college graduates in the Congo after the Belgian withdrawal.

The problem has been well summarized by Dr. Wilbur Schramm in a special report to the Fund for the Advancement of Education. He refers to the frequent assertion that in this country we have a so-called education explosion, meaning a great increase in the number of school-age children. He points out that our education explosion is a mere toy pistol compared to what is going on in Africa, Asia, the Arab states, and Latin America. Sixty states in those areas are grasping for nationhood and trying to accomplish in a hurry the social and economic growth that older nations took centuries to accomplish. While we recognize that the education problem is important, these nations feel that it is crucial to their development. Well over half a billion people must be taught to read, write, and master simple computational skills. Hundreds of millions of people must be brought to accept new practices in agriculture, health, and home management. The occupational and mechanical skills of millions more must be brought up to the requirements of new industries, public works, and service occupations which are waiting to be created. This whole complex of needs calls for vast literacy teaching programs. School systems will require major expansion. And totally new efforts at service training and community-development instruction will have to be undertaken.

Not only is it a matter of life and death for nations to develop a system of education, it is a matter of determining the course of the world. There are few forces as gigantic, and as fraught with cruel and tragic disappointment, as the expectations and aspirations of underdeveloped countries. Their educational crisis is truly dramatic, and will require the application of everything we know and much we have yet to discover about the learning process and about educational systems.

These then are the forces making for educational change: the population and information explosions, the unparalleled change in virtually every aspect of life, and the aspirations of the 2 billion people of the developing world. They require, above all, a totally new approach to the idea of education. For even as we grapple with these problems through traditional methods, they are exceeding our capabilities.

THE TECHNOLOGICAL RESPONSE IN EDUCATION

A large number of educational materials, technologies, and methods are being re-evaluated or newly developed to form systems through which teacher and learner can interact. The nature of computer technology—the storage of information and its manipulation and distribution—makes it inherently important to these systems for education. But immense obstacles must be overcome before effective systems can be put into action. The materials are crude, the technologies are inadequate, and the teachers are not ready. To provide effective educational systems requires answers to questions that are seldom asked and almost never answered. Some of these questions relate to but go beyond education itself. They involve social processes that have come to achieve major importance only within the past few years. Obstacles have been created partly by the great technological advances of our times, but they are partly susceptible to technological solutions. "Partly" should be emphasized because essentially the obstacles reside within mankind and society's institutions, including the educational institutions and the business community that serves them.

Educational Institutions

We have not decided on the fundamental purposes of education in our age, even though we are profoundly aware that education is of the greatest relevance to the evolution of our society. Perhaps one key problem is that neither the teachers who go on strike, nor the parents of a ghetto child and a suburban child, nor the rioting students, nor most others within or outside the educational establishment have really determined what kind of society we want. Most of us only know that we don't want things as they are or as they might become in the event of change. This inadequate perception of purposes has deep roots in a society wavering between simplistic solutions and despair of any solutions at all. If we can't decide on purposes, how can we instill the motivation to learn in the disaffected children of the rich and in the alienated children of the poor? Indeed, it is probably true that young children's learning need not be motivated by large social questions. But those who determine what and how and to what ends they should be taught must examine these issues.

Some people within our institutions of education have given thought to means and ends. But, as John W. Gardner points out in *No Easy Victories:*

We like to think that institutions are shaped to the best vision of the best men in them, and sometimes they are. . . . But that is not the only way that institutions get shaped. Sometimes they are simply the sum of historical accidents that have happened to them. Like the sand dunes in the desert, they are shaped by influences but not by purposes. Like our sprawling and ugly metropolitan centers, they are the unintended consequences of millions of fragmented purposes.

These fragmented purposes as they affect education— these influences—are not only exerted by teacher, parent, and pupil. They result from other incidents and responses, such as those that over the past five years alone have increased the federal government share of educational financing from 8.9 to 13.0 per cent, while reducing the local share from 35.7 to 31.8 per cent. The President and Congress have been enacting far-reaching programs far removed from local problems, while local citizens confronted with conflicts and expenses close to home have rejected education bond issues. Fragmented purposes result from trends extremely difficult to assess, such as those that have made our nation's universities turn to federal sources for more than two-thirds of their research funds and that have made great schools—Columbia, Princeton, and M.I.T.—dependent on Washington for more than one-half of their total budget expenditures. They result from outmoded concepts pervading the education of teachers themselves, from the priorities of research and development (R&D), which have kept federal R&D expenditures on education to less than one-half of 1 per cent of total federal R&D expenditures, from the economic factors that over the past 10 years raised the price of hardcover books at a rate twice as fast as the average of all other prices, from the interests of businesses, which have precipitated some to take a reckless plunge into the educational field. It is evident that these fragmented purposes or influences reach education from areas far removed from the educational institutions that must serve as the arena in which both the purposes and the methods of teaching are tested and decided.

Above all, the student—whether in a Headstart program or in industrial training—has been largely ignored. To a large extent, so has the teacher's function in respect of the student. Yet, our most thoughtful educators know that learning is an individual process, which has meaning only if the student comprehends and is able to use the information the teacher tries to get across. If the school cannot understand or apply the information, the teacher, in effect, has not taught, and the educational institution has not performed its functions.

The purposes of institutional functions—the motivations for learning and the methods of teaching—are among the primary questions with which we must concern ourselves as a society. Then, teacher and pupil can get to work on the difficult task of fulfilling the purposes. The processes of learning can be identified, and the materials, technologies, and methods to facilitate the learning processes can be improved. Perhaps Ralph Waldo Emerson, who had his well-documented doubts about education, nonetheless identified better than most the needs of educator and student: "Our chief want in life is somebody who shall make us do what we can." But then, on another occasion, he wrote: "I hate quotations. Tell me what you know."

Educational Systems and Their Future

We know that society has always had educational systems. In one sense, a teacher and a pupil or a book and a reader can be defined as an educational system. But what concerns us here are educational systems with more complex interactions among diverse elements.

Right now, educational systems make use of materials—textbooks, slides, films, and audio and visual tapes—that make use of technologies—printing, still and motion pictures, radio, television, computers, and related input/output devices. Teachers are involved as individual tutors, as Socratic discussion leaders, as lecturers before audiences ranging from a few to thousands. Some of the more advanced systems, using combinations of innovative techniques and technologies that are experimented with today, are discussed below. But first, it is useful to take a brief look into the future.

At some point in the near future, our understanding of the biochemical and electronic factors in learning is likely to become a part of the educational system. Experiments in laboratories indicate that memory and perception involve chemical processes and that there are quantifiable biological differences in brain tissues that are exposed to various types of learning environments. There is some evidence that knowledge can be transferred between individual beings through tissue extracts. Learning or memory exercises during sleep appear possible through electronic stimulation.

There is considerable controversy about whether we shall ever be able to go to a drugstore to buy pills that will teach us medieval history and advanced algebra. It is not certain that we will be able to plug ourselves or our sleeping children or grandchildren into devices that will assure us and them of awaking in the morning with a full comprehension of the subjunctive in Latin. Above all, it is not known if we should want to do so or if we should want to instill motivation or achievement orientation into children or adults through synthetic means. However, there is little doubt that what we are beginning to understand about these biochemical and electronic processes can help us construct environments and programs—systems—conducive to learning.

Similarly, what we must learn will be affected by and will affect the systems. For example, even as now fairly unsophisticated information retrieval and calculating devices are available to us, we can expect, perhaps within one or two generations, what Dr. Vannevar Bush calls "man-machine symbiosis" where the vast memories and calculating speeds of computers will become direct extensions of our mental processes. When this happens, memory may serve not so much as a limited repository of facts, but as a tool to open up almost unlimited data banks. There is some question even today regarding the function of memory. Tomorrow, memory may be confined more or less to serving personal needs and, importantly, to providing the processes for the acquisition of data.

This somewhat speculative look into the future is most important to an appraisal of the educational questions facing us today; it points to the need for flexible systems able to make use of new developments. At the same time, however, these systems must be clear in their purposes, so that they may teach what must be learned today and tomorrow rather than what it was customary to learn yesterday.

A growing variety of advanced systems are being considered, experimented with, and evaluated in educational and economic terms at this time. They are discussed here with a view to the estimates made and the questions raised in the following sections on the business of education.

• *CUES (A Computer Utility for Educational Systems)*, studied and developed through contracts from the U.S. Office of Education by IBM, General Learning Corporation, and Computation Planning, Inc., is perhaps the most easily implemented of the advanced systems. Actually, it goes just a few steps beyond the use of computers for such administrative purposes as student and classroom scheduling and payroll and record processing. It is suggested that a nation-wide network of computer centers could provide, in addition to the above administrative services, courses in fundamental computer concepts, a number of problem-solving exercises involving direct student access to computers, and vocational training in basic computer skills to some 90 per cent of U.S. students in public elementary and secondary schools. At a later time, some of the more complex educational systems concepts, such as computer-managed instruction and library services, could be integrated into CUES.

• *CMI (Computer Managed Instruction)*, studied and developed primarily by Systems Development Corporation, the New York Institute for Technology, the American Institute for Research, and the Westinghouse Learning Corporation, is envisaged as a further step in the use of advanced systems. It would help the teacher to individualize the instructional process through the computer processing and evaluation of each student's capabilities, progress, and responses to various types of instruction. It would not involve the computer in the learning process itself but would guide the teacher in the use of learning materials best suited to individual student needs.

• *CAI (Computer Assisted Instruction)*, studied and implemented in varying degrees by a large number of school systems, universities, and businesses, is potentially the most complex and expensive of the advanced systems. It puts the student into direct dialogue with the computer, in which the educational materials are stored. Basically, two types of CAI have been identified by the Committee for Economic Development in its report *Innovation in Education: New Directions for the American School*. The "drill-and-practice mode" would have relatively simple computer programs, "involving a set of repetitive exercises dealing with one learning event with which the student is already familiar." The "tutorial mode" would have complex computer programs "involving a combination of programed instruction and drill-and-practice, with the additional capability of random access." As is evident from these descriptions, the first type would have a potential more or less limited to the student's need for rote exercises. The second could be applied to highly sophisticated learning processes, with the student answering through individualized sentences and graphics and with further material being presented in direct response to the quality of the student's answers.

• *Audio-visual instruction,* studied and implemented in various forms and combinations throughout the United States, cannot really be called an educational system. However, it is potentially a part of any advanced system. By definition, it includes computer-initiated graphics, as well as television, films, and slides. It can be individualized, either by providing the student with an audio-visual display responsive to the student's immediate interaction with the system, or by directing the student to a generally available audio-visual program. For example, the "tutorial mode" of CAI might provide the former, while CMI might help the teacher decide to have the student attend a particular series of television lectures—which might be "instructional television" or even general educational television.

It should be quite evident that elements of all of the advanced systems described here can be combined in numerous ways and that eventually the chance will come to integrate the technologies and concepts still in the laboratory, some of which were treated above. The manner and extent to which the systems are implemented depends on economic factors and educational decisions. An educational system, of course, is composed not only of technologies and materials but also methodologies and, above all, of personnel. An advanced system can be thought of as the most cost-effective mixture of these components, compatible with the economic means available and the social purposes decided upon.

Educational Technologies

Technological developments give promise that, in the course of the next decade, highly effective educational systems can be created that would alter totally the future processes of education. What are the technological developments that stress such systems' potential? Among those that appear most significant are the following

1. Voice recognition on the part of the machine system allowing not only activation of the system by the voiced command of the individual learner but also the interpretation and evaluation of the content of the spoken command.

2. Live displays that permit the user to see a continually changing graphic display of subject matter in the form of graphs, printed text, and photographs.

3. Machine intelligence developments, which have already provided us with examples of "intelligent" behavior on the part of computers in their reaction to their environment and to human commands.

4. Real-time systems with large numbers of input/ output devices for communicating with the system in an on-line manner.

5. Huge random-access storage of graphics as well as digital information permitting entirely new orders of magnitude in the library that can be stored within the system.

Such improvements, particularly in the man-machine interface, are making possible increasingly easy, natural communication between students and machine systems, so that we can begin to think in terms of computer-based systems playing a vital role in the educational process. At the same time, developments in time-sharing techniques should make such systems feasible for even the smallest schools or groups, and developments in communications will make it possible to link such systems over ever increasing distances.

Time-sharing will be of special importance because of its cost-reducing potential in computer usage. Even current technology allows a single central processor to give almost instantaneous access to large numbers of users with different programs. Since each user actually requires only a fraction a second of a computer's processing time for each inquiry, others can be served before there is any noticeable time lag in the response from the machine to the first user. Thus, costly computer time is shared by many. The advantages of this are obvious for educational systems in which hundreds or thousands of students perhaps each with an individually tailored program, simultaneously receive computer-assisted instruction. Major further advances in the multi-processing and multi-programing capabilities of computers are expected over the next few years. Finally, communications improvements are expected to make the time-sharing concept even more flexible in application because relatively idle machines would stand ready to take on users from various places if the local equipment should suddenly become overloaded.

It should be pointed out once more that technologies themselves do not make or run an educational system. Such a system is activated by decisions on educational purposes and is built on methodologies. It involves materials and personnel. In the final analysis, an educational system without students to teach is as superfluous as an electric power grid with no lights to light and no machinery to supply with energy. And this brings us back to the fact that, if the learner has not learned, nothing has been taught, and if the learner has learned what is useless or wrong or has been adversely affected by the educational process, incalculable harm has been done. Yet we must look at the nature of technological developments and probabilities, and at the equipment they will make possible, in order to gain an understanding of the educational problems and opportunities inherent in them.

Interaction of Technology and Education

Major continuing change must take place in our educational systems as a result of the forces described earlier. But, in addition to these forces, the interaction of educational technology itself with current or traditional educational systems is going to change these systems and the nature of education. In order to understand the role that educational technology will play, it is necessary to understand this process of dynamic interaction—a process that is going on all about us, yet has no name. It is an important phenomenon in our time.

Shortly after the electronic computer was invented, a statement was given wide circulation to the effect that all the computation in the country could be accommodated on a dozen—and later fifty—large-scale machines. That prediction was wrong not simply because it underestimated the number of calculations taking place. It proved wrong in large part because the existence of the computer changed what we do as well as provided a new way of doing it. In short, there was a dynamic interaction between the innovation and the system into which it was introduced.

This process can be likened to the Hegelian dialectic. If we take an initial problem as a thesis, the antithesis is the response evoked in solving the problem. The synthesis found in the resolution of the problem involves activities that generate new problems. The new problems are usually wider in scope and more complex in detail. The solution to the new problems becomes the stage for further development.

At first the computer appeared to be primarily a device to do a quicker job on familiar problems of calculation. However, the use of the computer was soon extended to new tasks and new problems. This extension led to new designs and new computers with new capabilities. Although we have not reached the top of this spiral, we already have a radically different conception of the present and potential role of computers in our society. They are changing society, most notably in ways not originally suspected.

Another striking example of the technological dialectic is found in rocketry. The first successful efforts at rocket propulsion went largely unnoticed; the major need for the rocket developed well after the rocket itself. The needs of modern warfare stimulated the cycle of interaction. The faster speeds produced by rocket propulsion created a need for new materials to withstand the heat generated by friction. New methods of guidance were also required. The development of new materials and new guidance systems opened up the age of space exploration. The present explorations of space are being used to a large extent to gather information that will be fed back into the system of design and use of rockets. New problems are now expected as part of an evolving system.

The skills and techniques created at one stage in dynamic growth are not ordinarily lost; they are usually incorporated in skills and techniques operating at higher levels of complexity. The second and third generations of computers, for example, have not lost the capabilities of the first generation; instead, those capabilities have been integrated with a set of new capabilities.

The effect of this kind of dynamic interaction is already discernible in our educational system. Our systems as they now exist were developed, or have evolved, in response to certain needs and influences. They, in turn, helped to create a society whose needs are met less and less adequately by these systems. A further stage of development is essential and can be expected.

THE BUSINESS OF EDUCATION

It is not hard to understand the growing interest of business in education. Already the market for textbooks, audio-visual aids, materials, and certain technologies and services is well above $1.5 billion annually. But fundamental change within the market toward systems using advanced technologies has been slow and has fallen far behind the expectations held by business at the beginning of the 1960's. Also, the difficulties involved in bringing about fundamental changes are proving much greater than foreseen. The realities of the business of education are complex, and much of the information we have is deceiving.

It is evident that the market for advanced educational systems over the next ten years or more will be large, but it will not be anywhere near as large as either the gross factors of demand or expenditures for education may indicate. Even the more experienced businessman can be deceived. Also, the investment required for successful entry into the market is already proving to be considerable.

The landscape is littered with the failures of ventures too confidently entered into and with high hopes too lightly raised.

To act in accord with the realities, business must be ready to learn what the market for advanced educational systems now consists of and what it can develop into over the next decade. This means learning both about educational financing and about the basic processes of education.

Financing is relatively easy to discuss, and a fairly good indication of it can be given right now. Educational processes is a far more difficult subject. It requires costly research and development by qualified people and a profound sense of responsibility. It involves seeking answers to the large institutional questions raised earlier, as well as to the detailed questions pointed out below. First, it is useful to reinterpret the forces making for educational change.

The Context for Educational Demands

In broad terms, the demand for education is determined by three factors: the number of people to be educated, the amounts and types of information produced and needed, and the funds devoted to education. However, each of these factors is made up of a number of phenomena.

The number of people to be educated is determined not only by population statistics but also by the length of time spent in the process of education and re-education. Thus, in the two decades from 1957 to 1977, the school-age population (five to twenty-one years old) is projected to increase by 49 per cent. But over the past decade alone, the number of people completing at least twelve years of primary and secondary education has risen 85 per cent. Over the next decade, this figure will grow another 33 per cent. The number completing at least sixteen years of formal education has risen by 69 per cent over the past decade and will do the same over the next. The increase of those enrolled in part-time and less formal educational and training programs is impossible to measure accurately, but is believed to equal the increases cited above, in terms of time spent in the educational process. It is interesting to note that by 1977 the number of people expected to receive college and graduate degrees (1.3 million) will be nearly as large as those who received only high school diplomas in 1957 (1.4 million).

The amount of scientific literature published in the United States over the past three centuries has increased by a factor of about 10 every fifty years. From one journal in the 1660's, it increased to ten by 1750, to one hundred by 1800, to one thousand by 1850, to ten thousand by 1900. We are passing the one hundred thousand mark now. In electrical engineering, the amount of information available over the past two decades has doubled every six years, from 3,000 pages published in three journals in 1946 to 30,000 pages in forty-two journals in 1966. *Chemical Abstracts* published 178,898 abstracts in the ten-year period 1907-16. In 1966 alone, it published 215,000 abstracts from 11,500 journals originating in one hundred countries. The annual subscription price of this publication has risen from $6 in 1940 to $12 today. In the United States, research libraries double their holdings of scientific literature every seventeen years.

One half of the scientific research done in the United States since 1776 has taken place over the last eight years, thus giving rise to the growth of interdisciplinary information complexes such as biochemistry, biophysics, astrophysics, cryogenic engineering, and econometrics as well as to the creation of occupations outside the scientific disciplines. Some of these, demanding previously nonexistent information for learning and for application, are solid-state circuitry specialist, system analyst, human factors analyst, real-time programer. The number of scientists in the old and new disciplines doubles every twelve years. The growth of other specialists is even greater. For example, in 1951 there were a few hundred computer programers; in 1961 there were 20,000; and by 1971 we shall need 300,000.

The obsolescence rate of the most advanced information is such that within ten years about one half of the really important knowledge an individual in these fields has acquired is outdated. Thus, while the amount of information produced and the number of those needing it doubles every ten years, the demand for this information rises even more quickly. A striking aspect of this problem was given recently by a vice president of one of our nation's three largest banks. Addressing a group of about thirty of the top executives of his bank, he stated that the obsolescence factor in the knowledge of his computer systems people already is so high that he has great qualms about introducing the latest technologies. He put the useful life of the knowledge of his technological staff at three years.

The funds devoted to education must be discussed not only in terms of direct expenditures on public and private school systems, various training programs sponsored by industry, labor, trade associations, and government, and correspondence school courses, but also in terms of the educational benefits and needs generated by at least a part of the money spent on research and development. In the United States, expenditures for research and development are about $25 billion annually today and may exceed $40 billion in another ten years. It is probable that education, for at least a time, may receive less output for each additional dollar invested. Thus, total expenditures for elementary, secondary, and higher education have more than doubled to $50 billion annually over the past decade and are projected to increase to $70 billion by 1977. But little or no growth in educational productivity is visible in these figures. This situation will continue until major breakthroughs are achieved.

The context for educational demands provides a broad framework for more specific issues. It represents, so to speak, the universe within which questions can be raised and outside of which estimates cannot be projected with accuracy. However, in too many instances, businessmen have equated the limits of this universe with the market for advanced educational systems. Although this may become so in the fairly distant future, it is not so now and cannot be expected over the next decade.

Educational Financing

Expenditures for education are growing enormously. But what is the real nature of this growth? Most additional funds are being used to meet current needs, ranging from teachers' salaries to school lunch programs. In 1957, the current expenditures of elementary and secondary schools comprised 72 per cent of total outlays. By 1967, the current share had risen to 82 per cent, while the share of capital expenditures decreased from 26 to 14 per cent. This occurred in spite of—or because of—a 33 per cent enrollment increase. Institutions of higher education fared no better. In the face of a 116 per cent enrollment increase between 1957 and 1967, current expenditures took an increasing share of total outlays, while capital expenditures accounted for a share that decreased from 24 to 20 per cent. In other words, American schools are running hard in order not to fall behind the demands placed on them. The application of advanced technologies could help our schools get ahead in this race. But where will the initial and the on-going capital investments in research, programing, and hardware come from?

Sources of funds might be sought in various areas. Perhaps they reside in specific federal programs, such as Assistance for Educationally Deprived Children, for which nearly $1 billion was appropriated in 1966, and educational research, for which some $70 million was expended in 1965. But the former is a stopgap program of sorts, and the latter is very small. Other specific federal programs are small also, for example, $15 million for educational television facilities in 1966.

In 1968, it was estimated that business has invested some $75 million in the development of computer-assisted instruction. Additional millions are being spent on the development of simpler technologies and methods. And a beginning has been made on laboratory experimentation with biochemical processes. Also, there is increasing academic talk about—if not yet much investment in—the investigation of basic learning processes. The debate between B. F. Skinner and Noam Chomsky is an example.

In 1965, foundations spent an estimated $14 million. The Foundation Library Center believes actual expenditures may be slightly larger, but they are not much, as yet. A total of estimates from various sources indicates that funds expended on educational research are only a fraction of 1 per cent of all expenditures for education. This compares, for example, with the 5 per cent that many corporations spend on research and development in other areas.

This is the financial picture. Although huge expenditures are made, little seems available for investment in advanced educational systems and even less for basic research. However, the picture could change, if the long-term growth trend of stopgap expenditures, which do not increase educational productivity or quality, could be reversed. Is this likely? The following discussion of the urgency of fundamental educational questions and of the cost advanced educational systems and potential cost savings may indicate both of the widely felt need for such a reversal and of the economic considerations that could help to bring it about.

Educational Processes

The introduction of educational technologies without adequate research carries the same dangers as the marketing of inadequately tested drugs. Educational experimentation, in the last analysis, is human experimentation. As such, it involves immense responsibilities. Not only money is needed but time—and the will to spend both—

for the responsible determination of what can and should be done.

Among the questions that must be answered are those involving motivations and methods, as well as institutional questions. We know too little about what must be learned and how learning does or should take place. What standards do we work from? The concepts of fixed intelligence are being abandoned. It is felt that individuals, individually treated, can transcend physiological, psychological, and cultural limitations.

From this point, we approach the area of motivations— basic ones and those that relate to the teaching method. Perhaps it is not desirable to make learning too easy. Is there a danger that certain learning systems will stifle curiosity or reward noncreative thinking? Is it possible that, with computer-assisted instruction or biochemical and electronic learning stimulation, "we are about to replace natural stupidity with artificial intelligence?" This question has been raised by Ralph W. Gerard, Dean of the Graduate Division, University of California, Irvine.

What are appropriate mixtures of materials, technologies, and teachers for the individual student at different stages? In the words of Nathaniel M. Cartmell, Jr., of McGraw-Hill: "Materials don't teach—teachers teach— and materials only implement the teacher." Of course, this holds true for the technologies as well. The problem is how best to implement the teacher.

The teaching method depends on what is to be taught and on who must be helped and motivated to learn. Some educators believe that the primary need is to instill the desire for and to teach the techniques of learning. The obsolescence rate of knowledge and the continually changing character of work and life, they say, make the accumulation of facts and specific skills useless, if not harmful. Others point out that certain data and a number of basic skills are essential and must be acquired and retained throughout the individual's educational process. Combinations of methods must be used. It is believed by some that the learning problems encountered by the beginner who tries to acquire elementary knowledge are not too different from those of the postgraduate who tries to grasp the most advanced concepts newly presented to him.

From these considerations emerge the problems of individualized instruction. The first attempts, through programed learning and the so-called teaching machines on the whole have not proven successful. What, if anything, does this tell us about computer-assisted instruction?

As we have seen, we are dealing with human experimentation. The way we teach, the instruments and systems we apply, the age at which we launch our children into the formal educational complex will all have a profound effect not only on what our children learn but also on their psychological make-up. It is no longer a question of pure method, of John Dewey versus the German pedagogues or of the permissive school versus the disciplinarian. These are gentle issues of the past.

The fundamental questions we face are not questions for tomorrow, after the technologies and systems have been installed. They are questions for today. They involve every child in Headstart, every student learning the "new math," every industrial trainee for a new or changing job. Unless an adequate beginning can be made in answering them, the available measures of educational demand and of financing are of little use.

Over the past few years, education has seen a confrontation between unsophisticated buyers and sophisticated machinery. While there have been some companies impatient to sell advanced technologies for education, some consumers have been equally impatient to possess these technologies just because they are available or appear prestigious. Now, however, the balance of forces may be changing. The number of school districts has declined rapidly from 47,000 in 1958 to about 21,000 today, and as the resulting individual units become larger, their purchasing practices appear to be growing more sophisticated. The right questions are beginning to be asked. An increasing number of districts are cooperating with universities, foundations, business enterprises, and federal agencies in experimental programs to test new educational methods and technologies, as well as new forms of community relations to the educational process.

The Costs of Advanced Educational Systems

What do the school districts, as well as other educational institutions and the growing number of corporations with internal educational programs, have to deal with in terms of costs for advanced systems? We have already pointed to the meager financing available up to now for research and experimentation and for the installation and operation of these systems. Therefore, costs are a crucial factor in the economics of educational change, and in the markets for advanced systems that business is exploring.

First, one can look at what various types of currently developed or suggested systems are estimated to cost and what they can be expected to cost in the future. They already have been described in this chapter, and they provide a good example of the wide range of investments in advanced systems.

CUES, the simplest of the advanced systems, involving administrative data-processing, a basic course for computer technology, selected computer-assisted problem-solving exercises, and vocational training in computer usage would cost an estimated $750 million to $1.1 billion annually on a nation-wide basis. This estimate does not take into account any cost displacement or savings in administration.

CMI, involving computer assistance to teachers in guiding and administering the instructional process, has not been systematically studied with a view to the costs of national application. However, data developed from the CMI Project Plan (Program for Learning in Accordance with Needs), which has been functioning in eleven representative school districts in the United States, as well as from other sources, indicates that it could add between 3 and 5 per cent to the $600 annual public school expenditure per pupil. This would mean from $900 million to $1.5 billion per year. It does not include the potential for CMI use in institutions for higher education or for advanced study and refresher courses, and it does not take into account any cost displacement or savings in teacher time.

CAI, involving direct student interaction with computer systems, is subject to the widest spread in cost estimates.

The Committee for Economic Development report, estimates that CAI extended to 16,000 out of the nation's 21,000 public school systems would cost between $9 billion and $24 billion annually, depending on whether the simpler "drill and practice mode" or the "tutorial mode" of instruction were used. One hour of CAI per student per day is envisaged. Cost displacement or savings in teacher time are not taken into account.

Audio-visual instruction involves a fairly wide range of cost estimates. The CED report gives an annual range from $265 million to $1.5 billion for television alone. The Diebold Group, Inc., projects a 1975 market potential of $537 million for all kinds of audio-visual equipment and material, as against $292 million in 1965.

The system costs given here are based on the current state of the various technologies involved. This is of significance in estimating future costs. For example, more than 70 per cent of the CED estimate for CAI systems can be attributed to current hardware costs. The report comments that "the record of United States industry for ingenuity in the rapid development of new technologies strongly suggests the likelihood that costs will be brought down in this field in the not-too-distant future . . . as the experiments with [computer] use demonstrate its capabilities and potentials in instruction."

Experiments now being undertaken at the University of Illinois, using a CDC-6600 computer on a time-sharing basis, indicate a CAI cost per student-hour of 25 cents, or a nation-wide cost of $1.5 billion annually on the CED assumption of CAI use for 150 days of the school year, one hour per pupil per day. The cost of 25 cents per student-hour represents almost a 50 per cent reduction in the estimated current CAI costs of systems being tested elsewhere throughout the country—for example in New York City, where the cost is now 47 cents per student-hour. It represents a significant indication of the potential for future cost reduction in advanced educational systems hardware.

A related aspect of the cost factor, insofar as CAI is concerned, involves the dramatic reductions that can be achieved through the intensive use of computer time. A recent study undertaken at George Washington University under a contract with the Department of the Army estimates that the total cost of CAI per student-hour ranges from $3.73 for a 32-terminal system operating ten hours a day, twenty-four days a month, to 20 cents for a 448-terminal system operating eighteen hours a day, twenty-four days a month. As developments in communications technologies bring closer together the costs of transmitting over long and short distances (the former are being reduced much more rapidly than the latter), it becomes economically possible to utilize CAI equipment across time zones. On the basis of 20 cents an hour, and with the CED report's usage assumptions, the nation-wide cost of CAI would be $1.2 billion annually.

However, it is questionable that one hour of CAI use per pupil per day, as posited by the CED report, represents anything close to the total revolution in educational processes envisaged by our leading educators. Even if one hour a day of instructional television (which, according to the CED, could be accommodated within the present range of educational expenditures) were added, there would still be no provision for four of the six hours of a regular school day. Also, there seems to be no room in these estimates for CMI, which would be an important element of advanced educational systems.

In summary, there are a number of systems, ranging in cost from less than $1 billion to nearly $25 billion annually on a nation-wide scale. These systems (or at least the cost estimates relating to them) are mutually exclusive to a large extent. Also they generally represent only a relatively small introduction of advanced techniques into the educational process. The cost estimates, with two exceptions, are based on current technological costs. They exclude possible major expenses (or savings) in the area of construction. They do not consider potential cost savings in teacher or administrative time, and they are limited to public elementary and secondary education.

To place these estimates in long-term perspective it is useful to look at the implications of a resolution adopted by the American Association of School Administrators in February, 1968:

> . . . traditional methods of developing and introducing curricular ideas are insufficient to enable the educational system to meet the increased and urgent demands upon it. We therefore urge that "moon-schools"—pilot centers for the development and testing of new educational strategies and structures —be established by districts or combinations of districts.

Dr. Edward C. Pino, Superintendent, Cherry Creek School District, Englewood, Colorado, estimated that a "moon-school" with an enrollment of 6,500, ranging from pre-school to post-graduate and adult education students, would cost about $150 to $175 million to construct and operate for the first five years, or $30 to $35 million annually. On the basis of experience with general educational expenditures, at least 85 per cent of this cost can be attributed to salary and construction expenses not directly related to the cost of introducing advanced technologies. Thus, what has been called the "creative application to all known media" of educational technologies might cost some $4 million or $5 million a year for each of these projects. Two thousand "moon-schools" would serve about 20 per cent of the population that could directly benefit from them and would cost $8 billion to $10 billion annually for advanced technologies. To serve all the potentially interested population would involve $40 billion to $50 billion annually in advanced technological costs, and $300 billion to $350 billion annually in total educational expenditures. Of course, such a program is not contemplated, at least over the next decade or two. But when one considers that expenditures by regular educational institutions are projected to increase threefold, from $23.3 billion to $70.2 billion annually in the twenty years from 1957 to 1977, and that the percentage of the gross national product devoted to education has more than doubled since 1950, it is not impossible to envisage annual educational expenditures of several hundred billion dollars annually by the beginning of the twenty-first century—the time to which the "moon-school" concept addresses itself.

Clearly, the "moon-schools" represent total advanced education systems for use by all segments of a population, which would be getting almost cradle-to-grave education.

Their universal adoption is not probable. Rather, various institutions are likely to provide education ranging from kindergarten through in-house industrial training. But the point is that we have explored a wide variety of what is being done, experimented with, and proposed, in terms of cost estimates. The nature of the staggering differentials exposes the need for a fundamental re-evaluation of what must and can be done.

It seems likely that one of the basic approaches to this problem can be found in the industrial sector's employee education, training, and retraining programs, in which the cost effectiveness of various educational techniques becomes a major determining factor in their use.

In a 1966 survey of one of the major corporations in the United States, 16,000 of its employees (18 per cent of the employees in the divisions covered by the survey and 13 per cent of the total work force) were engaged in 415 training programs. The programs were in ten categories: management, sales and marketing, finance, science and engineering, systems and automatic data processing, clerical activities, production, safety and maintenance, orientation, and other. Forty-four per cent of the courses used training aids other than blackboards, the most prevalent being audio-visual devices. Total educational cost per student-hour was $9.20—as compared to some 38 cents per student-hour in public elementary and secondary schools; 41 per cent of this cost was attributable to training equipment, training materials and instructors' salaries —with 30 per cent of this, or about $1.12 per student-hour, spent on equipment and materials.

In spite of the high costs per student-hour, 65 per cent

of the managerial respondents to the survey indicated that training programs in science and engineering and safety maintenance could be made more effective through the use of additional trainings aids. In these programs, such aids were already being utilized more intensively than in most other programs. The threat of job obsolescence was reported to be the most significant stimulus to the establishment of training courses for skilled and semiskilled employees. Thus, industry in its own crucial training programs appears ready to make substantial expenditures in order to achieve effective employee education. That one major corporation has been willing to spend nearly three times as much for equipment and materials alone per student-hour than the total cost of a student-hour in our public elementary and secondary school systems is of some significance—even though, of course, the total of 24.3 hours per year each employee was engaged in training programs is only about 2.4 per cent of the hours the average student spends in school each year.

To relate this discussion of the costs of advanced educational systems to the market possibilities for business, one final factor deserves mention—potential cost savings. Although savings are of low priority on the list of reasons for the introduction of advanced systems, they can help in stimulating their financing. Only one example will be given here.

Estimates are that some 40 per cent of an elementary and secondary school teacher's time is used for various clerical, housekeeping, and monitorial duties, and by 1977, there are expected to be some 2.6 million elementary and secondary school teachers. At their projected salaries, the cost of performing these duties will come to some

$10.4 billion a year. Insofar as new systems, such as administrative data processing and CMI, can reduce or eliminate this kind of work, up to $10.4 billion annually would be available for the purchase, installation, and application of these new systems in pre-college schools. It is likely, of course, that most of such potential savings would not actually be taken out of the nation's educational budget. Rather they would be considered as an additional and quantifiable indicator of how advanced systems can assist in raising teacher productivity. It has been the general experience with the introduction of improved technologies and methods that they seldom result in an actual reduction of costs, but they improve the quality of the product or service of the user. A brief example of how this may affect education is provided by recent IBM research. In a CAI course on data processing, student completion-time averaged 22.5 hours as against 30 hours under the classroom lecture method, and the students learning with CAI did 5 per cent better on the final examination than the conventionally trained control group.

A number of conclusions may be drawn from the discussion of costs. First, national figures are dependent on too many variables, in terms of the types of systems that may be utilized and the cost estimates and projections attached to them, for the development of a really meaningful estimate or range of estimates that would enable us to measure either the cost of or the marked for nationwide advanced educational systems. However, for the purpose of discussing the *potential* market for such systems, it is possible to say that several billion dollars annually would be involved in developing and operating advanced educational systems on a nation-wide scale. The effectiveness of such systems would depend almost wholly on the answers to the previously raised questions regarding social purposes, educational methodologies, and institutional responses.

Second, it is possible to make cost estimates for individual school districts or groups of them, once they have decided what they want in advanced systems. This decision is also important in assessing the market potential.

Third, a good sector to watch is the use of advanced systems by industrial firms for employee education and training. There the cost factors are under close scrutiny, and educational purposes are more closely drawn. Also, the great proliferation of educational and training programs within business firms makes them a major element of the potential market itself.

Fourth, in measuring costs against financing, it is evident that advanced educational systems costs should and will to a large extent replace the costs of conventional education, rather than be added to them. Nonetheless, the increases in quality they make possible will undoubtedly raise the cost of education per student. Expenditures (in constant dollars) per student in public elementary and secondary education have increased some 33 per cent over the past decade. A continuance of this rate over the next ten years should be able to pay for a considerable amount of innovation and technology, in addition to covering other rising costs.

The Market for Advanced Educational Systems

In order to assess the market, it is necessary first to define it. There is much controversy regarding what actually can be sold in that market, how much can be sold, and how soon. Therefore, it seems best to define the market as a potential market. With this qualification, there appears to be some consensus as to what can be sold.

The potential market is for total advanced systems—not just technological hardware and materials, but programs, methods, and other software, as well as the training of teachers and administrators to use these items and services. As previously indicated, this should involve several billion dollars annually on a national scale within a time frame that is realistic for business planning—ten to fifteen years. However, probably more useful for business efforts would seem to be an evaluation of what individual school districts or groups of them are willing and able to do, in order to direct marketing efforts to such districts.

There are certain interim measures, however, of the national market, divided into products and services on the one hand and user groups on the other. These can be useful for decision-making by business. Now, and probably for some years to come, certain materials (textbooks, programed instruction texts, audio-visual hardware and software and teaching machines can be sold in predictable quantities. In addition, CAI systems can be marketed to a limited extent, as can certain services related to the materials. The Diebold Group, Inc., projects that this real market will grow from $1.4 billion in 1965 to $2.7 billion in 1975. It should be emphasized, however, that this is only in part the potential market for total advanced systems. The real market is likely to be considerably larger but is subject to the variables already discussed in part in the preceding pages. However, it is really this potential market that is of primary concern to the developing business response in education. The extent to which the potential is realized depends on the quality of the business response, which is probably the single most important variable.

The Business Response

That the business response to the challenges of education has fallen short of success is far from surprising. It is a pioneering effort in the new relationships among private enterprise and government and other entities resulting from the impact of technology on society. In the words of Charles E. Silberman, writing in the August, 1966, issue of *Fortune:* "Rarely have United States corporations assumed a role so fraught with danger for society, or so filled with responsibility and opportunity."

This is a role that business is going to have to fill in a large number of areas calling for the application of advanced technologies—if the private sector is to continue as a vital force in our society. Thus, we have here a case study with far-reaching implications for the future. A summary of the failures encountered may help in the analysis of business plans for the last third of this century, because the field of education partakes of a most fundamental and advanced characteristic of our age—the need for various disciplines and enterprises to combine their resources in an attempt to tackle new problems systematically from a number of directions.

What have been the salient points of the business response? The educational market too often has been perceived only in gross terms. Its components, its current and future needs, and the resultant requirements for serving it have been analyzed without due attention either to the obstacles to specific changes or to the pressures that can help to turn the need for change into an effective demand for change. Many of the individual business moves were poorly planned—that is, staffed with the wrong people, financially unsophisticated, and dependent on technologies developed for related but actually quite different purposes. Yet the general direction of the response has indeed taken account of the need for interdisciplinary and cooperative approaches. This is important because it encourages the hope that the specific problems can be worked out within a framework that is essentially sound.

What has happened has been a great casting about for mergers, acquisitions, and other joint arrangements among electronic manufacturers, publishers, manufacturers of educational materials, and mass communications media. This has brought together, among others, General Electric Company and Time Incorporated to form General Learning Corporation; Radio Corporation of America and Random House; Cowles Communications, Educators Association, and College Publishing Corporation; and Columbia Broadcasting System and Creative Playthings.

These new ventures were usually based on the expectation that the electronics manufacturers would supply the ready-made technology that would be combined with the in-house educational know-how of publishers, communications media, and producers of educational materials. The results then would be packaged for sale to the educational market. Unfortunately the know-how, where it actually existed, could rarely, if ever, be combined with the ready-made technology. The successful combination of old educational experience with a new technology, originally designed mostly for noneducational purposes, actually requires a kind of thinking and questioning that we are only beginning to understand. There are few people capable of it as yet.

In the meantime, however, some of the packages of technology and know-how were being sold to unsophisticated buyers. Before long, it became evident that little of value was to be found in these packages. The investments of the sellers in their development and of the buyers in their purchase were lost. As a matter of fact, most of the new business combinations have until now produced no viable packages at all. Their investments, if not lost, have not yet paid off. Some of the joint ventures turned to other things. Others—for example, RCA, persisted and developed new packages from scratch. But it is unclear to what extent the newly developed packages actually resulted from the joint ventures.

Since the original purchasers of educational packages were badly burned, the most responsible firms that hope to enter the market are fearful that the further peddling of worthless packages may discredit the whole field of advanced educational technology. This would not only be a loss to responsible sellers but a tragedy for education, which is in dire need of technological innovation.

It is difficult, of course, to devise a responsive, over-all business approach to the educational market. Many kinds and sizes of enterprises are involved. Their capabilities—financial, technological, managerial—differ. Their goals in the market differ. But, clearly, a way must be found by the private sector to chart a responsible course.

The large investments required to produce technologies that precisely meet the needs of education must be made. In doing so, the fundamental questions on educational purposes and processes must be explored. New talents must be developed. Finally, standards on experimentation with and application of the technologies must be set—just as in medicine. All this requires the expenditure of money and time. Francis Keppel, a former U.S. Commissioner of Education, writes in his recent book, *The Necessary Revolution in American Education:*

> Change is not automatically for the better. In education's history new fads and cults have often given the appearance of progress while failing to transform education for the good of society. It is imperative to review all programs for change with a critical eye for the consequences, *particularly in a time of revolution, when the pace of change discourages pause for reflection.* [Italics added.]

It is in this light that conclusions are drawn for the consideration of private enterprise and of our educational and government institutions.

CONCLUSIONS

The conclusions and suggestions that follow address themselves to the need for a new kind of relationship among private enterprise, educational institutions, and government. Each has capabilities and responsibilities, some of which can be exercised jointly and others of which adhere primarily to one. However, a paramount force of our age is the interaction among previously independent disciplines and social entities. And this provides the thrust for these thoughts.

Indeed, the role of private enterprise in education is a

case study of the future. It involves a fusion of private and national interests that we are already beginning to see in areas of endeavor as widely separated as the development of oceanic resources and supersonic air travel. If atmospheric pollution affects the oceans or if the oceans' organisms can no longer counteract newly created imbalances in the atmosphere, are even these areas still to be considered widely separated? Still more evident today are industry's interests in skilled manpower and in sophisticated consumers for new products and the national interest in an educated citizenry. And these interests are translated into the education industry's stake in the markets for advanced educational systems and the national stake in the usefulness of these systems.

There are several useful responses by private enterprise, educational institutions, and government.

• Local or regional cooperative arrangements among individual businesses, school districts, and institutions of higher education could be established with substantial government funding. Such arrangements would develop experiments and train personnel in basic, high-quality educational research. The scarcity of trained professionals in research has been a major obstacle to progress in the use of advanced systems. Directly related to this is the need to educate the educators themselves in the effective application of these systems. Also, priorities and responsibilities for educational financing and goals must be set. This can be done on a local basis, initially, although national coordination is desirable at some stage. Standards of quality and compatibility among educational technologies also can be drafted first on the community level, although here national coordination would seem essential to make them effective. Probably of greatest importance would be the setting of ethical standards, not only to help the user to understand the cost-effectiveness of the various technologies and techniques he buys, but to assure a thorough evaluation of their impact on the student—especially the very young.

• Nation-wide cohesion for these efforts could be provided by a coordinating body. If existing educational or private sector groups are unable to undertake such a program it may be advisable to form a new association composed of businesses and educators engaged in the development and marketing of advanced educational technologies. Or the task might be given to a national commission on research, innovation, and evaluation in education, as recommended in the Committee for Economic Development (CED) report, *Innovation in Education: New Directions for the American School.* This commission is conceived of as an "independent, nongovernmental agency, chartered by Congress, which would receive both public and private funds." The CED sees it as a "citizens commission," broadly representative of our society. Among its additional activities could be the promotion of the study and formulation of legislation in the copyright area to protect the incomes of authors and publishers while providing educators and students the full and flexible access to information which advanced technologies make possible.

• Coherent federal government policies in the wide range of areas affecting the quality of education should be established.

Such policies could lead to the elimination of contradictions in federal policy which, for example, pour billions of dollars into education, while the Internal Revenue Service rules that any schooling that leads toward a degree or professional advancement is not tax deductible. The effect of this has been that, in order to receive tax benefits in a society that desperately needs maximum individual efforts in the acquisition of knowledge, one must prove that one's educational self-betterment will be strictly limited and undertaken only to hold on to one's present job.

Also such policies might look to the conscious development of the United States as a world educational center, perhaps making knowledge itself a major export product of the future. One specific action toward this end could be the encouragement of "high-level scientific commuting" (as suggested by Professor Derek J. de Solla Price) to less-developed areas of the world through the provision of meeting places and occasions for conferences with local scientists and educational leaders. Another could be U.S. participation in an international "Brain Bank," as proposed by the International Association of Universities.

Education must meet extraordinary, unprecedented demands in our age of accelerating social change. The survival of societies and individuals depends on our winning what H. G. Wells almost fifty years ago had the prescience to call the "race between education and catastrophe." But merely to run the race as fast as possible will not bring victory. We must try to understand where we are going and what will happen to us on the way. We must face fundamental questions and answer them, for the ultimate, visible purpose of life itself is at stake—the spiritual and physical welfare of the individual human being. Thus, we are confronted with the need for responsible action. New institutions and new means must be devised to apply technology to the explosive educational issues which technological advance itself has thrust upon us.

Chapter 3

INTERNATIONAL DISPARITIES

The second case study deals with the technological elements of economic, cultural, and political disparities among nations. New processes have been altering trade balances and widening the gap between the rich and the poor. New industries, based on the most sophisticated technologies, are creating cultural lags among nations. Political barriers are exacerbating these problems.

A key to the resolution of disparities among nations is the international transfer of technological know-how, innovation, and application. The so-called technological gap between the United States and the rest of the world has especially subtle but dangerous characteristics. It shows the difficulty of transferring the substance of technological advances among nations—even if these nations appear essentially to be on an economic par with each other. It is possible that the newly emerging international corporations may provide a bridge for the transfer of technology.

This chapter is based on an article originally published in Foreign Affairs, *the quarterly journal of the Council on Foreign Relations.*

Technological change is both a cause and an effect of the differences in life styles manifested by nations and cultures. Insofar as it is a cause, it increasingly divides men and societies from each other. As the pace of technological development quickens, it gives rise to envy among those it appears to pass by. Also, to the extent that the capabilities that technology places into the hands of men are universal, it places increased power into the hands of the elite in the most backward nations while depriving those nations of effective defenses against outside interference. Thus, it threatens to divide societies against themselves as well as against each other.

Insofar as technological change is an effect of differences among nations and cultures, it probably can be traced most directly to educational roots. That is, whatever underlies the motivations for and the practices of education is largely responsible for the state of technology in different societies. As educational systems enable more individuals to use technology, they tend to become similar to each other. Since education is fundamental to cultural distinctions, systems leading to higher levels of technological achievement also tend to erase differences in life styles.

From the perspective of international affairs as from almost every other perspective, technological change has profound human consequences. It threatens to cause divisions potentially fatal to individuals and societies at the same time that it faces man with the loss of those traditional identities that help to provide much of the substance of life itself.

Quite obviously, this is not all that can be said of the

role of technology in international affairs. Its military potential for destruction haunts us: the word is "mega-deaths." Its potential for homogenization disturbs us: the word is "communications." Its potential for life and achievement gives us hope: the word is "understanding." The problem is how to achieve a positive interaction between technology and man. By discussing a specific aspect of the international question, in the manner of a case study, we may achieve understanding more quickly than by attempting a broad and necessarily superficial survey.

One of the most subtle, yet dangerous, aspects of the growing disparities among nations is found among the industrialized parts of the world. While the great and widening gap between the industrialized and less-developed nations must be recognized and dealt with, it is becoming clear to a number of us that successful action to assist the latter depends on economic and political parity among the former. The industrialized nations cannot undertake a united mission for global development when they themselves are drifting apart from each other. Yet the difficulty of transferring the substance of scientific and technological advances from one nation to another, even in the industrialized world, is great. The emergence of the international corporation may provide an answer to certain basic elements of this difficulty.

For some years now, the disparity in the production and application of advanced technologies between Europe and the United States has been the subject of mounting concern to statesmen and to leaders of the business community on both sides of the Atlantic. Prime Minister Harold Wilson has warned that Europe is about to succumb to a kind of "industrial helotry" to the United States. Charles de Gaulle, Ludwig Erhard, and Franz-Josef Strauss have spoken in similar terms. And J. J. Servan-Schreiber's *The American Challenge*, which raises the specter of a technologically based U.S. hegemony over Europe, has been the best-selling non-fiction book since World War II in France. Indeed, the disparities between Europe and the United States—especially as they express themselves in technologically related matters—provide a focal point for the ambivalence with which we are viewed by the non-Communist nations of Europe. U.S. power is feared; it is also needed. Part of the fear stems from that need. Part of the need is to remove the cause of fear. The time has come to sum up the diagnosis and direct our attention to the formulation of practical policies in Europe and America.

THE REAL AMERICAN CHALLENGE

The nature and causes of the technologically related disparity should be approached through an examination of the economic, educational, cultural, and political difficulties attending European attempts to advance and apply scientific and technological knowledge. But it is desirable first to examine the ways in which the United States enters into and influences this picture. On the one side, there is within the United States itself the apparently irresistible force of invention and application of invention, partly based on government financing and carried through by huge and growing corporations. On the other side, there is the carry-over of this phenomenon into Europe by way of American enterprise.

Not only is the United States the home of giant corporations, which can afford the costs of basic research and development and the risks of innovation, but it also has a long lead in the establishment and growth of relatively small, new enterprises created for the development and exploitation of advanced technology. The technologically based businesses are found commonly in the areas of electronics, acoustics, optics, solid-state physics, high-energy physics, instrumentation, metallurgy, pharmaceuticals, and plastics. Europe has no such tradition of broadly-based industrial entrepreneurship, and this, combined with its somewhat rigid social structure, hampers the formation of new business based on the latest technology. Also, venture capital for exploiting new technology is in short supply. The European capital market still is poorly developed and organized to provide the initial financing needed by smaller, innovative enterprises. Another major obstacle is the lack of concerned and involved governments providing assured markets for the products of these new enterprises arising out of advanced research. By contrast, in the United States, the government is often the main or only initial customer, providing market support at the crucial stage of establishing the business.

The carry-over of American activity to Europe can be measured by the size of U.S. direct private investments and the sales of U.S. subsidiaries in Europe. Both grew three times faster than the rate of European economic growth over the ten years following the formation of the European Economic Community (EEC). Although in any one country sales of American subsidiaries still represent less than 5 per cent of total economic activity, the increasingly obvious penetration of American goods, ranging from toothpaste to computers, provides a basis for European alarm. When the then generally favorable U.S. trade balance with Europe is added, it is easy to understand how fears of dependence on the United States find a response in both European government and business circles. In addition, of course, American products manufactured under license represent an important factor in European consumer and industrial markets. The latest data available show a 5-to-1 advantage ($251 million to $45 million annually) for the United States in receipts from licensing agreements.

At the beginning of 1951, U.S. direct private investment in Europe stood at $1.7 billion. Fifteen years later, at the end of 1965, it was $13.9 billion—an eightfold increase. The largest absolute increase—more than $9.7 billion—took place during the latter half of this period, after the signing of the Treaty of Rome, which established the EEC. Significantly enough, however, during this latter period, new U.S. investment in the EEC was less than in the rest of Europe. It is quite possible to say, therefore, that although the formation of the EEC triggered the American juggernaut by calling attention to the possibilities of the European market, since then U.S. corporate giants have straddled Europe, inside and outside the EEC, apparently unaffected by a political and economic division that is most fundamental to the European psyche. American business, with its international character and huge resources, not only has been able to derive greater benefit than all but a few European corporations from the supranational climate and potential within the EEC, but even has ignored successfully the continued split between The Six and the rest of Europe.

THE REAL PROBLEMS IN EUROPE

Thus, a measure of discouragement enters into the European attitude—a discouragement that leads not only to hostility but to an abdication of responsibility for taking practical steps to meet American competition. In the view of Peter Hilton, of the Institute for New Products, Inc., there is "an inclination to cut back research and development allocations by European industry on the premise that they would only be rediscovering what the United States has already discovered."

Research and Development

An important element in the disparity is believed to stem from differences in research and development. Undoubtedly, research and developments expenditures in the United States exceed those in Europe; the figures are something like $25 billion versus $10 billion annually. On a per capita basis, the ratios are 3 to 1 vis-à-vis the United Kingdom and Germany, 8 to 1 for Belgium, and 25 to 1 for Italy. But when calculated in terms of relative gross national product and purchasing power, these ratios are reduced. Further, the overwhelming portion of U.S. research and development expenditures goes into defense and space efforts, which are only indirectly related to U.S. success in applying technology to commercial uses. How indirectly is an important consideration.

On the one hand, the U.S. government provides a market for companies in advanced technological fields and establishes a *raison d'être* for the pool of trained personnel that has been built up and maintained to serve this market. On the other hand, legitimate questions can be raised as to the effectiveness of government-sponsored research and development efforts in serving the real needs of society and of the international competitive position of the United States. Finally, there are clear indications that research and development in Europe is first-rate. As will be seen, its application and (in the words of the chairman of a major U.S. electronics corporation) "the engineering follow-through bears the burden of the difference in results here and there." In lieu of a full discussion, it can be stated that, whether the differences in research and development expenditures and quality are as large a factor in favor of the United States as may appear at first glance, there can be little doubt that they do help and constitute an element of some importance.

Management

Nonetheless, other elements are more fundamental. One is the prevalent—although far from universal—European attitude toward risk-taking. Competition and the consequent need to innovate generally are deprecated in Europe. Indeed, the role of European governments is often to protect against innovation, and private enterprises too generally prefer to let others do the hard work of breaking new ground, while hoping that future developments will not profoundly affect traditional ways of doing things. This attitude affects the most crucial problems of management and manifests itself in failures to relate inventive effort to market need, inadequate evaluation and development of markets, little or no product planning, and old-fashioned production scheduling. These managerial inadequacies appear to be the result of major policy weaknesses in respect to managerial appointments, promotion, responsibilities, and incentives. Consider the following examples of such inadequacies.

• The electronics division of a large European firm functioned entirely without product planning that would put it in touch with the market. It consistently lost money for several years. After the recommendation was made that a top managerial post for product planning be established, it took one year before the company's directors accepted the need and another year before the position was filled.

• The French Compagnie des Machines Bull lost a prosperous business (and still is in deep trouble, in spite of massive infusions of capital and know-how from General Electric) primarily because it disregarded its competition in the computer field and miscalculated both its market and its own capabilities. It is most likely that entrepreneurial decisions permitting sound management in these areas could have retained for Bull a significant and independent position as a computer manufacturer.

• ICT, the British-owned computer manufacturer, until recently did not have a management sufficiently strong to bring together the diverse parts of its merger-built structure. The primary managerial areas to suffer were product planning and marketing.

• European (and particularly British) companies developed some first-rate control devices for magnetic-tape controlled machine tools. But, disregarding actual market needs, they concentrated on very high-precision and, therefore, high-cost controls. A major U.S. firm, in developing control equipment for the American market, found that considerably larger tolerances were quite acceptable, hence used a different and much less expensive technology to produce a relatively low-cost control system. As a result, the firm not only has a major market position in this country, but also is taking the bulk of the European market away from the European suppliers.

• In many European enterprises, the failure to innovate is not considered a cause for censure, but the failure of an innovation might be. In such an atmosphere, business and profit planning and the consequent search for and adaptation to markets hardly exist. Key scientists and managers rarely have equity in the companies they serve. There is little or no financial participation in risk-taking and innovative ventures by the men who can make them succeed.

Some other examples serve to reinforce the conclusion that Europe's inadequacies do not reside so much in scientific and technological invention or research and development as in the availability of entrepreneurship, managerial skill, and capital for turning inventive genius into profitable innovation. Many technologies in the aerospace industry, including the swing-wing plane and the hovercraft, were initially developed in Western Europe but are being applied successfully in the United States. The same is true of laser technology and cryogenics. A majority of the inventions underlying the office copying-machine industry, in which the United States is dominant, can be traced to Europe—specifically France, England, and the

Netherlands. Fluidics, vital to engine control in supersonic jets, and holography—with wide areas of application including photography, molecular biology, mass data storage, and the direct transfer of handwriting into computer language—were originally European efforts that are now being put to practical use in the United States.

Patents

An examination of patents granted in various countries provides another approach to the nature and causes of the gap between Europe and the United States. It shows not only a lack of actual or intended application of inventions on the part of Europeans, but also a consequently growing gap in the inventive process itself. The countries selected for this examination are Belgium, France, West Germany, the United Kingdom, and Sweden, with Japan and the United States providing the basic comparison. Between 1951 and 1965, patents issued by these European countries to their own nationals generally declined. Excluding the United Kingdom, for which comparable data are not available, the decline was from 42,616 to 28,085 annually—or more than one third. In Japan and the United States, domestic patents increased greatly during this period—from 4,350 to 17,797 and from 39,606 to 50,332, respectively. In the European countries examined—West Germany excepted—patents issued to foreigners in 1965 greatly exceeded patents issued to nationals. However, in the United States, the number of patents issued to foreigners was only one fourth of those issued to American citizens, and in Japan foreign patents were one half of domestic ones. Between 1951 and 1965, U.S. patents formed an increasing percentage of all patents issued to foreigners in the European countries, with the exception of Sweden. Meanwhile, there was no substantial increase in the number of patents issued by the United States to nationals of the European countries, except West Germany. But U.S. patents issued to Japanese nationals jumped from virtually none in 1951 to nearly 10 per cent of all those granted to foreigners in 1965. Some of this increase may be ascribed to Japan's postwar recovery. But since nearly all of the increase took place after 1960, one must seek other reasons also. Japan has a competitive international spirit, which stimulates investment in development and application engineering and, above all, in managerial and marketing innovations that make the technology pay off. The Japanese have learned what Peter Drucker calls "creative imitation." Many of their patents carry already developed products and processes one or two steps further, improving quality, cost effectiveness of production, and marketability. And their adaptation of U.S. managerial methods—another instance of "creative imitation"—appears to be the driving force behind both the applications and the growth of profitable markets for them.

A major reason for the patent situation as it has been described resides in the complexities and incompatibilities of the various national patent systems themselves. These make the process of applying for patents in foreign countries both difficult and expensive. Such expenses, of course, are most easily borne and justified by American industry, with its relatively large assets and its desire to apply internationally the results of its own research and development. Further, there appear to be some fundamental weaknesses in the patent laws of certain European countries. As compared to the United States, Europe offers weaker protection for its patent holders. This not only discourages inventive efforts but also results in a secretiveness among inventors and their employers, which severely hampers the dissemination of information.

The Brain Drain

A phenomenon widely discussed in connection with the technologically related disparity between Europe and the United States is the brain drain. During the five years, 1962 through 1966, more than 60,000 professional and technical workers came from Europe to the United States. The yearly average has remained fairly steady, between 11,000 and 13,000. Among certain professions, up to 15 or 20 per cent of those graduated annually from European universities are emigrating and often they are the best in their field. These figures may change after the new U.S. immigration law, which removes the preferred status of Western European emigrants, becomes effective. However, even as this law went on the books in mid-1968, potential loopholes were becoming evident. Its impact may be minor. At any rate, it does nothing to ameliorate the basic, long-term reasons for the brain drain.

The reasons are not hard to find. Starting opportunities and salaries in Europe are far below what can be found by professional people in the United States. The scientists' and technicians' access to top management and to the decision-making process in day-to-day operations, as well as their eventual chance to rise to management positions, is much more limited in Europe. Financial participation in the results of innovative processes still is virtually nonexistent. Thus, a large number of European scientists and technicians are attracted to the United States by better pay, higher status, and greater opportunities for creativity and responsible decision-making. A fundamental aspect of these advantages is the so-called mission-oriented approach of American research and development.

Although far from all scientific personnel like to be tied to profit-making or otherwise tangible objectives, many find expression for their creativity, as well as financial reward, in this approach. American enterprise is known for tying creative endeavor to tangible objectives in the most advanced fields, especially computer and communications systems, aerospace, and certain areas of metallurgy.

The incentives given to potential European immigrants to the United States are summarized well by an excerpt from a typical recruiting ad in Europe:

> Employers will pay the full fare to the States for you, your family and belongings—probably offer you an advanced study course—give you staff support and facilities you never had before. The powerful American economy offers terrific prospects for technical people at all levels of experience. Major long-term projects opening up are creating new opportunities. The professional's role in research, development and manufacturing is highly valued in the U.S.A. Employers are more willing than ever to hire a man for his potential and give him lots of responsibility fast.

There is nothing really new in this. A similar situation was noted nearly a century and a half ago by Alexis de Tocqueville, who wrote in 1831: "To build a house, to run a ship, to manufacture an object, or to produce wheat the American people always found a way to use half the manpower needed in Europe. Hence, salaries are twice as high and this in turn draws always larger groups of immigrants."

A PERSPECTIVE ON DISPARITY

It must be remembered that European achievements are far from negligible in pursuits that lie just below the pinnacles of advanced technology. These pursuits are of fundamental importance to scientific advance and human progress, and though sometimes lacking in glamour, they reap great economic benefits.

The Pilkington glass process, developed and applied in England, has revolutionized plate-glass manufacture in the United States and the rest of the world. New steel-making processes found their first applications in Europe, and, at this late date, only some of them have been applied by the American steel industry, hampered by huge investments in old processes and serving a market affected by the introduction of substitute products. The development and production of the Philips color television camera is a major European achievement in the area of advanced electronics itself. The high quality of European automobile and pharmaceutical manufactures, and the superiority of Italy's pharmaceutical equipment are well known throughout the world. Although widely scattered, some of the most advanced and creative installations of computer and communications systems—that is, the software aspects of an industry that is becoming central to nearly every aspect of human endeavor—are to be found in Europe. Even though much of the equipment originates in the United States, its advanced application is a European achievement. One consequence of these European advances is that the U.S. share of world export of manufactured goods has been falling over the past decade. The shares of most European countries have more than held their own.

With regard to the brain drain, an examination by the European countries of what their critical manpower needs are as against what they are actually losing could well result in a revision of judgments regarding the real effects and seriousness of the brain drain. And it could resolve the question of the extent to which European scientists and technicians who return to their countries after a stay in the United States are subtracted from the brain drain total. Presumably, those coming to this country under government-financed educational programs are never included—except for the 1 per cent that meets the legal requirements permitting them to remain. But what about others who return after having gained valuable experience? Are they part of the brain drain? Also, Europe—like the United States—actually experiences a substantial in-flow of manpower from the developing nations. These persons come for additional training, but unfortunately they often fail to return to their homelands. Are they considered in the total assessment of the European problem? To what extent is the brain drain issue exploited (quite understandably) by the European scientific community itself to enhance the financial remuneration and the professional opportunities of its members, especially where governmental support is involved?

It is necessary to take a hard look at the development of American industry itself, both technologically and geographically. Hardly a day goes by when one does not read an account of the perilous state of some industry, its backwardness in applying the latest advances of science and technology, and the reluctance of the financial community to risk capital on new processes and necessary development. Hardly a day goes by without one hearing that, in some major corporation, managerial caution or lack of adequately equipped personnel hampers the achievement of breakthroughs to new products and vital services.

Within the United States, there are more significant and varied disparities than between Europe and the United States. The brilliance generated by a few centers on the east and west coasts cannot blind us to backwardness in Appalachia and other regions. The brain drain from the Midwest to California, Massachusetts, and New York is greater than the whole world's loss of trained personnel to the United States. There is a remarkable similarity between the complaints of political leaders and businessmen from Illinois, Indiana, and Michigan, and those in England, France, and Italy. Natives of these states and nations are educated at great expense only to be lured away by the glittering areas around Berkeley, Boston, and the Middle Atlantic coast.

In due time, of course, these inequalities within the United States are likely to disappear—and even be reversed—through the natural forces of the U.S. competitive economic system and the judicious application of government policy. But the problem does exist. The State Technical Services Act passed by Congress in 1965 is intended to spur state activities to provide local businesses with information on, and the ability to apply, the latest technological and scientific advances. The very existence of this act—as well as other legislation, including the establishment of productivity councils, the support of small business enterprises, and regional development schemes—is a reminder that, however far we have reached into the future in certain areas and industries, there are large parts of the United States and of the U.S. economy that have not yet been brought out of the past.

It is true that IBM has between 60 and 65 per cent of the European computer market, that almost all European long-distance aircraft are built in the United States, that the Concorde supersonic aircraft being developed by France and Britain may be outdated within three years after coming off the production lines by the supersonic transport that will be built by the United States, and that the brain drain of the 1950's and 1960's toward the American economic and technological colossus may be as serious and significant as the exodus of scientists, philosophers, and poets from Europe during the 1930's and 1940's. Nonetheless, U.S. technological superiority in a number of industries has not been achieved with ease and it is not certain to remain. The areas in which the United States lead are important, but they are not the only determinants of economic and political power. In some cases, they are far-flung salients only precariously supported from inadequate positions of fundamental economic, educational, and political strength. Perhaps, rather than being the staging areas for further irresistible advances, they are only bargaining points. The advantages they represent are not necessarily permanent or even long lasting. The dollar gap changed within a few years into vast dollar and gold holdings by West European central banks. Hiroshima has become one of the greatest cities of one of the world's most powerful industrial nations.

AN APPROACH TO DISPARITY

There is little doubt that a disparity does exist between Europe and the United States in certain areas of the most advanced technology and science It is caused by a number of European managerial and financial inadequacies, as well as by an outmoded educational system, social immobilities, and political barriers. The consequences of this situation are the legitimate cause for concern.

Several things reasonably might—but probably should not—be done. The United States, in a Marshall Plan type of program, could subsidize the West European acquisition, both private and government, of American scientific and technological knowledge and managerial techniques for applying the results of research and development. The United States could, for example, transfer organic parts of its great academic-industrial complexes to Europe. These complexes could be made to grow, training and employing Europeans exclusively. The operative conditions for such assistance could be the accelerated admission of the United Kingdom and her EFTA associates into the Common Market, the swift rationalization or unification of West European corporate, tax, patent, and social service laws, and, perhaps, even the establishment of a unified European currency under a body similar to but more powerful than the old European Payments Union. The United States could revise its immigration laws to exclude any potential West European immigrant certified by his or her native country as vital to that nation's interest. It even could expel any foreign residents in the United States who had not yet either applied for or attained citizenship, if their services were desired by their native countries.

It is possible to construct a historical rationale for such a course of action. It is evident, however, that these things probably should not be done. This is not 1947, with Europe prostrated by war and ready to accept America's tutelage in return for the assistance needed to get back on its feet. For more than a decade now, Europe has been an increasingly successful rival of the United States in the competition for markets and political influence. Any attempt to enforce conditions—other than payment in hard cash—for U.S. assistance would serve only to raise the temperature of still smoldering resentments left over from the days of American hegemony. Indeed, Europe, in order to maintain its competitiveness, will have to learn to increasingly apply the advanced products and techniques of American science and technology and the methods of American management to the production and marketing of those items in which it excels.

What, then, should Europe do to prepare the economic, political, and educational environment for corporate growth? The following steps should be considered.

• Establish technological and scientific priorities and managerial goals on a country-by-country and on a supranational basis. This would imply, specifically, the application of information, communications, and other hardware and systems techniques to the expansion of European industries and their worldwide markets. It is necessary to go considerably beyond the $500 million government financing of private computer manufacturers planned in

Britain, France, and West Germany over the next few years. These are national investments, aimed principally at national markets. They tend to discourage mergers and other forms of cooperative and competitive action, and reinforce the continued development of incompatible and inadequately diversified systems, which fail to meet the need of European industries for the latest technology. Similarly, this type of national financing is likely to provide computer manufacturers with little help in meeting competition outside of Europe.

• Conclude intra-European political agreements to enact compatible corporate, tax, patent, and social service laws, which will permit the formulation of goals for business mergers and marketing. Recent data indicate that the United States, with 55 companies having sales of over $1 billion annually, enjoys a 3-to-1 advantage over Europe in this regard. However, in respect of companies with sales of over $250 million annually, the United States had a somewhat less forbidding lead of 2 to 1—248 United States companies against 119 European firms. Once the harmonization of European legal systems becomes a reality, one could reasonably expect a substantial increase in the number of European companies of the latter size, well able to afford large-scale research and development and marketing expenditures. But probably even more important than the matter of size for individual businesses is the formulation of competitive marketing strategies and the development of appropriate equipment among technologically advanced European industries. This process must take place on a supranational scale and requires a supranational legal and entrepreneurial climate.

• Organize effective efforts both by government and private business to hire U.S. talent for such purposes as the improvement of European communications and other technological infrastructures, the establishment of management training programs, and the specific application of research and development to the production of marketable goods and services.

• Accelerate and expand the revisions begun in the European educational system. This is fundamental. Dr. James A. Perkins, president of Cornell University and chairman of the President's Advisory Committee on Foreign Assistance Programs, wrote in the July, 1966, issue of *Foreign Affairs:*

> Perhaps no wind of change in Europe is more important than the revolution, just started, that will inevitably lead to the democratization and modernization of the schools and universities. Until this reform is completed, the European educational system will be the bottleneck that shuts off the development of Europe's manpower and shortens the life of its great dreams.

One of the major recommendations of the Deauville conference of May, 1967, was the creation of a European institute of science and technology in order to expand Europe's educational facilities to provide scientific, technological, and managerial training. These would graduate not only a large number of scientists of the highest quality but also a proportionately even larger number of second-level and third-level technicians and managers to serve vital supportive functions. For example, early in the 1970's, Europe will need 50,000 additional computer programers and 25,000 additional systems analysts—increases of 140 and 270 per cent respectively over 1966. Further, the modernization and expansion of existing institutions of higher education is essential. A number of other basic steps come to mind. One would be to establish academic chairs, research facilities, and student scholarships sponsored by business firms. On the basis of such grants, the possibilities of contractual relationships between students and business and between universities and business should also be considered.

In its role as both competitor and Atlantic Community partner, the United States should be ready to provide appropriate assistance to such European efforts. American cooperation could take the following form.

• Try to achieve a major increase in the financial participation of Europe in U.S. ventures. Of course, this is a two-way street: European banks, businesses, and individuals have to be willing to put up the money. Nonetheless, much more could be done to sell the idea of financial partnerships.

• Provide tax and other incentives for American corporations to establish additional research and development facilities in Europe. Such facilities would provide primary and secondary markets for scientific, technological, and management skills in order to slow down or reverse the emigration of newly trained European talent. As David Rockefeller has said: "The most important contribution that we can make to Europe's technological development . . . is to do more of our own exploratory research" in Europe itself.

• Contribute to European education in science, technology, and, above all, management training. Financial assistance by American businesses and foundations could be directed specifically to facilitating the exchange of professors between Europe and the United States, especially in management training. The direct participation of American businessmen in European management education can be a rewarding experience for both sides.

• Re-examine the Export Control Act of 1949 and its administration. This act has been repeatedly extended by the Congress in virtually unchanged form. Its existence, and certainly its administration, have made the United States an increasingly unreliable source of supply for equipment ranging from computers to printing presses. As American and European policies on East-West trade have diverged over the past decade, the Export Control Act has caused annoyance to the Europeans and a loss of export opportunities for American firms. Now that U.S. policy regarding trade with most Communist countries is undergoing a fundamental re-evaluation on the part of government and private business, it would appear an appropriate moment to remove the divisive and often self-defeating aspects of the Export Control Act. The frequently arbitrary decisions made in the name of this legislation have served to reinforce Europe's reluctance to depend on the United States as a supplier of much-needed advanced technology. Understandably, this situation is used to justify the uneconomic diversion of European resources into the development of technologies that could be more economically produced and supplied by the United States.

These suggestions are by no means exhaustive; new ideas and new forms of cooperation inevitably will arise. The form and extent of European integration that would make possible the needed harmonization of legal systems are left open, and how measures taken should be coordinated is best left to the affected parties. In any event, the emphasis should be on European initiatives, with active support by the United States. The first consideration of U.S. support should be U.S. interest in Europe as an equal economic competitor and an effective partner in world affairs.

The fundamental conclusion to be drawn from this discussion is that technologically related disparity should be a reason for neither European isolation nor European backwardness. It is not a manifestation of technological failure that Europe must overcome through the isolated development of its own technology. Rather, it is the result of European political divisions and of differences in managerial and financial capabilities between Europe and the United States. Also, it is an expression of natural comparative advantage in international economic affairs. Such advantage is subject to change by technology and its application as well as for many other reasons—economic, political, social, and the fortunes of war and peace. If the nations of the Atlantic Community understand and act upon this conclusion, the existing disparity need not widen or take on an importance it does not have.

As can be readily seen, the technologically related disparity between Europe and the United States is so fundamentally tied to the way in which business enterprise operates and to what it does that an approach to rectifying the disparity falls naturally into the following broad categories:

1. Removing the political barriers that hamper the formation and the operations of globally oriented enterprises.

2. Providing the economic environment for the growth of such enterprises.
3. Assuring both the training and the incentives needed by the managers of such enterprises.

Europe must have its own international corporations that can compete with those based in America. Eventually, however, it can be reasonably expected that the crossover of equity participation and the sharing of managerial responsibilities between Europeans and Americans in those corporations will result in the development of truly international enterprises. Parity will thus be established among the industrialized parts of the world. Japan and other nations, because of their recent successes, will be included in the growth of this newly powerful international economic force.

Even as this force develops and unifies the outlook and interests of the industrialized nations, effective policies for assisting the two thirds of the world's people who live on the edge of starvation can be initiated. Such policies undoubtedly will involve the transfer of technology, and they will make use of the power and experience of international corporations. But that is not the point. The point is that current divisions, fears, and suspicions among nations that should lead the world have frustrated the implementation of programs of assistance. If there is to be any hope of righting what Barbara Ward calls the "lopsided world," it will require a unified push from those who weigh so heavily in the balance. Unity requires the removal of the technologically related disparity that threatens to drive nations apart.

Chapter 4

THE TRAINING OF MANAGERS

Management education, the third case study in this book, demonstrates one of the most fundamental social responses to accelerating change. Technological innovation must be sponsored and marketed. Above all, it must be made to meet the realities of human needs. The education of society's managers in the private and public sectors requires innovations even more urgent and more specialized than in general education.

Management in business and public administration must increasingly be able to apply the tools of advanced technology to the challenges and opportunities created by the technology itself. This may well be the key to the question of whether our social system can catch up and cope with the accelerating pace of technological advance.

Thus, the leadership of society, and those

who teach the new leadership, must reassess the means and ends of teaching. The future of humanity rests in the hands of men and women whose future problems we can hardly guess, yet we must provide a conceptual framework for meeting these problems.

This chapter is based on an address presented upon the occasion of receipt of an honorary doctor of science degree at a special convocation, Clarkson College of Technology, Potsdam, N.Y.

When machines are in league with men, the soul of the alliance must be human, lest its ends become less than human. For practical purposes, even more important is the need for first-class human management of this league. Management must use the technology and encourage its development to serve human purposes. Yet the more sophisticated the technology becomes, the more difficult grows the task not only of utilizing it to the full but of directing it toward desirable ends—the satisfaction of real needs, the building of world peace, the preservation of individual rights, the conservation of natural resources, among the obvious ones.

This is a problem with far-reaching, international implications for management and managerial training. However, in order to get at the root of the opportunities and responsibilities of management education, we should start at home. We should do so because here is where the most rapid developments are taking place, and here is the base from which much of the global action starts.

In the United States, the giant corporation has reached its fullest growth, so far. The technologically based interaction between private enterprise and government has assumed the most fateful and subtle implications—ranging from the development of nuclear weaponry and space probes to the preservation of the natural environment and the protection of individual rights. The process of innovation and its management bear a recognizable American stamp throughout the world. Actually, when one thinks of it, it is rather surprising that in all U.S. lists of national assets, in all U.S. recitals of reasons for U.S. leadership—from democracy to raw materials to American know-how—one seldom finds listed American managerial skill. Yet it is this human, ephemeral, but real quality that is one of the greatest U.S. assets, for it allows Americans to turn the conditions of their land and times into a working asset, an asset of the most genuine meaning—not gold, though gold is important, not raw materials, though they are the stuff from which our world is made—the genius through which the spirit of American enterprise is today reflected. The more one sees of the world outside this country, the more deeply one can understand the thin but tough thread on which our leadership depends, and much of it is summed up in the understanding expressed by that simple word, management.

That changing science and technology pose problems is one of the most fundamental facts of life today. That science and technology provide sources to which one can go for solutions even as they create the problem is equally clearly a fact of the times. It is a part of what future historians may well come to consider the salient characteristics of this times—the human drama brought to a point of crisis by the rapid increase of scientific and technological advance. The sheer mass of scientific insight makes our problems so qualitatively different that it effectively differentiates the present from the world that existed until the outbreak of World War II.

QUESTIONS FOR MANAGEMENT EDUCATION

It is essential that questions raised for management education by these fundamental forces of change and science that are so rapidly altering the world as we know it be explored. That there will be major change in the development of men for management is in itself a fact that has thus far had too little attention.

Certain responses to the demands of this changed world are apparent—computer courses, degrees in systems technology, mathematical models, academic majors in data processing. But as important as these techniques are, they are only techniques. Computer courses explain that computers will change the way our businesses operate, but all too many of the courses in specific functional areas of management are presented as they have been for years. Far too little is known about the nature of the world managers will face and about the requirements these changed conditions pose for managers to succeed. Response has been superficial, to say the least, in terms of management education. This discussion will direct itself to three areas:

1. Identification of the characteristics of the changes that are important to management education.
2. Examination of the nature of the demands being made upon managers by a world with these characteristics.
3. Exploration of response, in terms of management education, and of the ways in which the usefulness of that response can be improved.

CHANGES IMPORTANT TO MANAGEMENT EDUCATION

Looking ahead more than a few years without having either the protective occupation of a science-fiction writer or being labeled a visionary always seems hard. Yet, when one looks back even a few years to the totally different world in which most of those concerned with management education were born, scarcely a thought is given to the forces that have been impelling man with increasing speed into an environment that not long ago would have been considered the world of a madman.

The conventional way of approaching the problem of training managers for a world of automation is to look at automation as a new tool and to say that the same problems will exist for the manager tomorrow as exist today and that the same kind of man and training are needed. Of course, automation is a new tool. But we forget that tools have had at least as much to do with making the man as did the man with making the tools. What we are about to do with science and technology will create entirely new kinds of enterprise to provide services and products that are today undreamed of. In a sense, this has been the course of all business history, but in many ways today's experience is unique because it has come so rapidly. The business opportunities change and depart rapidly; the scientific and technical aspects are much more important than has generally been true in the past; and the nature of the enterprise itself is really different. It is, therefore, worthwhile to look in some detail at the nature of the change that is taking place. One can identify many phenomena, and one can characterize what is happening in the world in many ways. For this discussion of management education, one can identify what seems to be three important phenomena.

Rate of Change

The rate of change—as distinct from the differing content of that change—appears to be the most significant phenomenon, for the increase in the rate of change is creating problems. These problems are yet largely unrecognized and unexplored. They are fundamentally managerial in nature, but they are obscured by the fascinating, frightening, and important content of the change.

The technological changes since the end of World War II are not a single burst originating from military work. They are the beginning of a continuum of fundamental change—a phenomenon that is likely to continue at an increasing rate for the foreseeable future. A detailed listing of them would fill large libraries—as it does at the Patent Office in Washington, at the Pentagon, at the Atomic Energy Commission, and at the headquarters of many corporations. Very broadly, they are in information and communications technology, transportation, biochemistry, metallurgy, synthetics. But what does this really mean? These areas involve work ranging from basic scientific inquiry to commercial technological applications. They all interact and are interdependent. They provide each other with the basic thrusts for further advances. Each is subdivided into a proliferating number of specialties, and these specialties combine within their fields and across the boundaries of the broader areas. Biologists can hardly do advanced work without computer specialists at their side. Computer manufacturers are increasingly dependent on neurological and other specialists from biochemistry.

So far as the society in which the manager manages is concerned, every factor making for change is at work to produce even more change in the future. Population is increasing in what has been referred to as an explosion. Thus the probability of innovation increases, as is indicated in more "simultaneous" discoveries each year that goes by. Education is on a scale never before known. With expenditures exceeding $50 billion annually in the United States alone, mass education on a high level is becoming a reality. Mobility is becoming a major characteristic of this more educated population. Communication in every form is fostering an environment that is both receptive to change and conducive to the origin of innovation.

The United States did not really begin to devote large-scale effort to scientific research and development until World War II. In 1940, a total of $280 million was spent on research and development in the United States. The military stimulus of World War II increased these expenditures to $1.8 billion in 1945 and to $3.1 billion in 1949. Most of the developments mentioned earlier are the results of the first decade of large-scale research effort. According to the Battelle Memorial Institute, whose economists have combined National Science Foundation, Bureau of the Budget, and other basic data, expenditures by industry, government, and universities reached $13.4 billion in 1960. By 1968, they totaled some $25 billion, and by 1975, such expenditures may well be in the neighborhood of $40 billion annually. Just think of the technology and products that can be expected in future decades as a result of such effort!

This increasing rate of technological change creates some fundamental problems for management. In part, the problems concern the processes by which management puts technology to work, and in part they concern the way the technological innovations affect the process of management.

Alfred North Whitehead wrote in *Science and the Modern World* that one of the important facts differentiating our time is "that the rate of progress is such that an individual human being, of ordinary length of life, will be called upon to face novel situations which find no parallel in his past. The fixed person, for the fixed duties who, in older societies was such a godsend, in the future will be a public danger."

How much more accentuated is this challenge and burden for the manager, who not only must face novel situations but must organize his business structure to utilize and incorporate constant change as a regular *modus operandi.*

The magnitude of the management problem posed by this sudden increase in the rate of technological change has hardly begun to be recognized as a problem at all. It is frequently viewed as a fortuitous or one-time situation and is attacked in a fragmentary manner in one industry after another. But this problem will soon begin to be recognized and discussed as one affecting the roots of management philosophy.

Complexity

John F. Kennedy once remarked:

> The fact of the matter is that most of the problems, or at least many of them that we now face, are technical problems; are administrative problems. They are very sophisticated judgments which do not lend themselves to the great sort of passionate movements which have stirred this country so often in the past. Now they deal with questions which are beyond the comprehension of most men, most governmental administrators, over which experts may differ.

The complexities of today's world and the tasks of managing it, whether in the public or private sector, pose by their magnitude quite new problems, even as they change the importance and character of persisting management problems.

To define a business in fundamental terms—not in terms of present products or services, but in ways that help to identify the genuine heart of the enterprise so that, as the environment and the product and the technology change, the enterprise goes on and prospers—becomes most important. The process of making decisions, as President Kennedy remarked, becomes enormously complex and different. It is no longer possible for men to rise to management having had firsthand knowledge and experience with every working aspect of the enterprise, for the enterprise itself is changing so rapidly. The different disciplines impose greater requirements for team approaches. An ability to make judgments in many fields becomes necessary. Judgment of scientific and technical matters is already looming large, but added complexities are evident. One man for one task is truly a thing of the past.

The Scale of Enterprise. While closely related to the complexity of enterprise discussed above, the scale of enterprise may usefully be identified as a significant, distinct characteristic. The phenomena, the problems, and the opportunities are seen best if some of the more advanced areas of technology are looked to. The supersonic transport is posing problems for risk capital that not even a whole industry can face without government participation. This situation is more characteristic of our times than most businessmen will as yet accept to be true, and the fundamental nature of the questions it poses with regard to the characteristics of private enterprise are as basic as any business or economic questions that can be posed today in the United States. Interestingly enough, like so many other questions of the most fundamental importance, (consider only the problem of what we do with the knowledge of the genetic code), this question is being almost totally ignored. This is one of the most interesting, upsetting, phenomena of our times, yet a condition that can be changed at will.

Scientific advance and technological innovation have caused U.S. corporations to be engaged in much more than just doing business abroad. They no longer only export; rather, they operate in many countries, and to an increasing extent, stock ownership and management are based in many countries. This poses unique problems of scale and of diversity inherent in scale.

From management this fact requires an ability to understand operations in entirely different political, economic, and social systems. Only a small part of the world operates under an environment of private enterprise. Most of the world has a far greater degree of government participation in business and, to an increasing extent, active planning than does the United States. Managers have to understand how to operate in such environments. Many factors remain the same, but many change. There are different ways of allocating raw materials and finished products and different organizational outlooks. Above all, there are different motivations for individuals, human beings respond in ways unfamiliar yet vital to the success of overseas ventures. Another perspective, closely related to human factors, is provided by the potentials of satellite communications, which has begun a process that will change totally our conception of the availability of people for the simultaneous communication of ideas as events occur and thus will change our sense of time. It will change the nature of what we consider to be markets for many areas of service, as well as for products. When we can advertise a product simultaneously throughout the world, we materially change the nature of the enterprise providing the product. The service of communicating the information becomes the basis for multi-national activity.

The questions of how we preserve entrepreneurial flair and creativity even while we increase enormously the scale of enterprise, how we provide risk capital of a scale necessary to cover the risk without eliminating the venture, how we balance the very real problems that generations of antitrust people have been concerned with—all these are inherent in the matter of scale.

One could identify other phenomena. For example, we today possess the means for achieving virtually any ends we wish, whether it be to travel the galaxy, mine the ocean, replace the human body, or educate, house, and care for the world's population. The fact of possessing these means brings to the fore the importance of the problem of choosing ends, for it brings us up against the question of deciding on the goals we as a society wish to pursue. These goals involve enterprises operating on an absolute scale unheard of in history.

THE DEMANDS UPON MANAGERS

How will management change as a result of the demands made upon managers by a world with these characteristics? Will the same kind of man who has risen to the top by making the right decision more often than the wrong one, when never having all the data necessary for making any decision, be the same kind who rises to the top when an extraordinary amount of data is available and the premium is on the ability to ask data pertinent to the decision at hand? Does a world of such complexity, scale, and rapid change as the one just described require the universal men of the Renaissance for managers?

Many questions come to mind when we look even a brief decade ahead, much less to the world in which today's students will have achieved their prime. What human qualities will be needed? How can one keep abreast of the changes? Will only mathematicians, physicists, and other scientists have a future in management?

One can begin by considering with the last question, for it is both important and typical of the questions facing those concerned with management education in a world of scientifically and technologically induced social change. Scientists will still need to be scientists and managers will still be managers. Tomorrow, as today, some trained in science will make their principal contribution in management, some in the management of science, and some in the management of business. Certainly, business managers of tomorrow will be better grounded in mathematics and the fundamentals of science than are today's managers—as tomorrow's average citizen will be better grounded in these disciplines, for they will be more clearly understood to be fundamental to our world. But the practice of management is a distinct profession. While the manager will need more than superficial understanding of the nature of science and technology in order to make proper enterprise and management decisions, while he will need to know more than he does today about the values and outlook of scientists because he will be managing more of them, while he will need to be able to exercise judgment in evaluating the business consequences of alternative technological developments, he will be trained as a manager. That is something quite distinct from training as a scientist. While he will make great use of the "management sciences," the emphasis will be on the "management."

However, the discipline of management will be more nearly stripped of the underbrush that today obscures the heart of the process. Tomorrow, less time will be consumed by the methodological problems of operating; more of the routine will be on magnetic tape. It will be less easy to avoid the hard realities of decision-making and particularly those of identifying problems and posing questions. The process of making decisions itself can obscure the hard work of posing the proper decision to be made, which will also continue to be the work of managers.

Three characteristics of management can be identified, the value of which is being enormously increased by the three types of change that have been described:

Substantive Knowledge

To begin, there is no escaping the need for substantive knowledge. One need not buy—much less put forward—the idea that one need understand only a process of decision-making and possess no substantive knowledge. The substance of what we need to know is changing very rapidly, and entirely different classes of substance are going to be more important than they have always been considered in the past.

First, knowledge of people and how they behave, their motivations, their response, and in the most human terms their desires, wants, goals, and objectives, is going to be the heart of the process. The manager who is intellectually more comfortable with machines than with people is going to be a less important part of tomorrow's world than he or the superficial writers who talk of human computers can even begin to understand. For when all is said and done, human desires shape the opportunities that spawn enterprise.

Second, knowledge of the processes of making decisions —logic, mathematics, management science techniques—is unquestionably going to become more important than it is today, and, anathema as it is to many, we had better accept this fact.

A third area of substantive knowledge changes continually—knowledge of particular technologies, product and service areas, business markets, economic opportunities, and so forth. There was a period—and some of us were born during it—when one could get along quite well throughout one's whole life by mastering this kind of substantive knowledge thoroughly in school That day has gone.

Entrepreneurial Understanding

One of the great business developments of the twentieth century has been the emergence of management as a profession. With the growth in the scale of enterprise and increased sophistication of management, we have come to rely in the United States, and to an increasing extent abroad on professional managers. This has been one of the great developments of our times and is responsible for far more of the condition of the world in which we live than most of mankind understands. The manager has taken the products of science and turned them into the environment of everyman. In the process, though, something has been virtually lost. It is business. As enterprises have been increasing in scale, fewer and fewer of the managers have been at the same time businessmen. The spirit of entrepreneurial flair—the peculiar characteristic that reflects the heart of enterprise and burns with varying degrees of intensity in the small businessman (who has more of it than many of us care to credit), as well as in the great creators of major industries—tends to be eliminated among the men who fit many of the other requirements that large-scale management systems impose.

As the routine tasks that have occupied the time of armies of managers and have often obscured the bright flame that burns at the heart of management are stripped away by information systems and the other tools of automation, there may well occur a refocusing of attention on the function of the entrepreneur. If this happens, it will be a particularly great boon to all the country. If we choose to develop the entrepreneurial flair and character of the individuals we also train for management, then we will make the greatest use of one of the most important parts of our national heritage.

The problem of preserving entrepreneurial flair in an environment of many large-scale enterprises is one of the most pressing and least considered questions in management education. The premium for a good answer keeps increasing.

Ability to Learn

Some education theorists feel that one of the most important educational consequences of the rapid changes so characteristic of the present is that the education a child receives at the beginning of his career must in the future address itself to imparting an ability to learn and concern itself less with the content of that learning. This matter must be dealt with in terms of the issues raised in Chapter 2. It is clearly a major factor in our response to the demands of our times. It is only mentioned here to point out the fundamental demand it places on management education in a world of automation.

THE NATURE OF OUR RESPONSE

How well have we responded to the changing forces of our times? Where have we erred? Where have we excelled? How can we improve the usefulness of our response? A number of problems for consideration and decision with regard to the process and substance of management education come to mind. Most of them relate, either directly or indirectly, to the need to keep informed throughout a lifetime in all fields relevant to proper management in an era of accelerating change. The roles of businesses and educational institutions in determining formal and self-educational requirements must be assessed. Consideration will have to be given to the trade-offs between time spent learning and time spent managing.

There is the question of the mix and timing among various disciplines: Should we simply train everyone as a scientist and then train scientists in management? Often enough this kind of transfer comes about naturally, by the choice or talent of the individual. But the institutionalization of the process may waste not only educational time and resources, but potentially good managers who would shy away from such requisites.

Directly related is the extent to which we should teach techniques instead of substance, and the extent to which we even try to teach the essence of what management is, for we have not yet tried to ascertain how the job of the manager will really change—what its essence will be. At least, we have not done so systematically. Will today's management training seem in a few years to be a crude excuse for time spent in what is supposed to be a disciplining of the mind?

Finally, there is the problem of whether we should have business schools at all. Perhaps we should only have graduate schools of business. Certainly relevant are the misgivings of Henry Adams when he wrote: "The chief wonder of education is that it does not ruin everybody concerned with it, teachers and taught."

The response we have made this far to the new demands of tomorrow's world has been extremely spotty. We are perpetuating one of the early follies, which was perhaps best summed up by Will Rogers when he said, "There is nothing more stupid than an educated man, if you get off the thing he was educated in." More often than not, we have responded with additional courses in all the new techniques, in addition to virtually everything else we had in our catalogues previously. We have looked to an increased range of coverage instead of to the fundamental, structural institutional changes that are going to have to take place, if our society is to respond—as it undoubtedly will—to the demands that are imposed.

What must we do? This can be answered after an examination of three areas. The first concerns the content or substance of what the manager must know. The deep roots of tomorrow's society are science and technology. We are unquestionably going to have to continue to give attention to doing a better and better job of teaching mathematics and science to management students—and this means teaching them in grammar school and in high school and in undergraduate work. Before they come to a business school, they are going to need solid grounding in mathematics and science. Along with this fundamental is going to be the question of content in the understanding of humans and how they behave in organizations and individually. This is the essence of the management problem.

The second area concerns the methods of management. Here much of what is today covered in business education can be grouped. The techniques of making decisions, the methods of organizing, the methodology of information system analysis and design—all these are of enormous importance, and we are going to have to continue to give attention to them in management training.

The third area concerns the form in which business education is taught. The real question we must address is with regard to the form of the institution of management education: What is handled in the primary and secondary educational system? What in college? What in the graduate schools? What in business itself? What by other new educational institutions that are being brought into existence to provide education throughout the life of the manager?

Already the response of society has been faster than that of the formal educational system, and we have seen a major volume of management training being conducted by institutions that twenty years ago were management societies and associations or that did not yet exist. The great growth of extension systems in universities and their wide use by managers active in business are two of the interesting phenomena of our time. They are the response of a system to a need. But the system that is responding is only in part the formal educational system. In part it is the system of society itself.

Considerable change is going to have to take place. The strife that will accompany such change is as clear as the fact that change will occur. For it is a peculiar characteristic of education—as of the labor movement—that a system that produces great liberals is the soul of conservatism (if not to say reaction) within our society. To continue to properly serve our society, the educational system must change as our society changes, and the change must be in the form of the institution as well as in the content of the curriculum. Learning how to learn, understanding human needs and human behavior, learning a basis for judgment when alternative scientific and technical schemes are the determinants for enterprise success—these are the imperatives for management education in the age of automation. Modifying, evolving, improving the present system is the most important part of a successful response. The ability of the institutions concerned to view afresh their own role and a willingness to alter the form of the institution are essential to success.

Chapter 5

THE LONG-TERM QUESTIONS

We must begin to anticipate earlier than we have in the past the problems of the future. Some of them already are becoming quite clear, and their impact can be expected to be so enormous as to require a long lead time for assessment and preparation. We are rapidly losing this lead time. It is evident that man's machines will rival and exceed many of man's intellectual powers, that individuals will be able to enter into a literally symbiotic relationship with these machines, and that, among other things, these machines may make it possible for man to affect the process of his own evolution. These developments are certain to produce a profound effect not only in the physical sense but in man's view of himself and his purposes.

A look at the history of scientific and technological change will help us understand that unexpected and inadequately perceived possibilities may be of greater significance than possibilities we can foresee. We must alter our standard approaches to the future in a way that will enable us to cope with what cannot be anticipated. At the same time, however, we must also try to anticipate as much as possible in order to provide a rational framework for our expectations.

This chapter is based on an address delivered upon the occasion of the receipt of an honorary doctor-of-laws degree at a Founder's Day convocation at Rollins College, Winter Park, Florida.

130

Throughout this book there have been hints of a future we find difficult to predict but must attempt to anticipate. The changes that have accelerated over the past two or three centuries and are propelling us into the future form part of a continuum. The problems we face today are the result of the past, just as they are the beginning of the future. Therefore, it seems appropriate to view our time from the perspective of both the past and the future. What has brought us here? Where are we headed?

AUTOMATION AS A HISTORICAL DEVELOPMENT

All too often, we accept the individual developments of technology as unique inventions, interesting and even significant steps in the evolution of a machine, or process, or discipline—a product of today's society. Only on occasion do we view them as part of a great continuum, which is bringing about a change in society itself. Yet that is what is happening. A study of the history of technology can provide us with an understanding of the process of technological change and of its consequences, so that we can begin to view the daily technological developments of today's world in proper perspective to grasp their meaning to our society.

Robert Heilbroner calls one of his books *The Future as History*. This title provides us with a useful challenge. If we can learn to interpret today's developments, and those we forecast for the coming decade, not as finite inventions or simply new machines but in the perspective of history, then we are in a vastly improved position to better conduct ourselves. Automation is an excellent case in point. For twenty years, we have been applying to industry, government, and business the technological developments fundamental to automation. The technology itself, of course, has been in evidence even longer than this, yet we have had to be dragged, screaming and shouting that there really was nothing new (or at least not both new and practical), every step of the way! Henry George, the rather eccentric economist, said: "The first thing they say is that it isn't true. And when its truth can no longer be denied, they say it isn't important. And when its importance is firmly established, they say it isn't new." We gain little from a conservative view of innovation, only the avoidance of fads, and lose the ability to lead in our use of technology, rather than letting the rapid changes alter our business and social structure at random.

The problem, in automation at least, is maintaining a rational basis in looking ahead. Technological and social changes are so great and the problems so numerous that, to properly look ahead, one must balance the difficulty of bringing about even simple change with the inevitability of great change. But this problem is not so pedantic or so difficult that we should shy away from it. How then will the facets of this many-sided development of automation stand up in the long view of history? Those that received the most widespread attention at first were:

1. Machines that performed, automatically, a long and often complicated sequence of functions—from pretzel-bending to the assembly of aircraft engines.

2. Transfer machines, a natural evolution of both the machine tool and the assembly line—the linking together of machine stations until not only hundreds, but now more than a thousand, metal-cutting functions are performed without human intervention.

3. Integrated systems of automatic machine tool, transfer devices, and automatic materials-handling equipment.

These often spectacular developments constitute much of the public image of automation; and, in particular industries utilizing long product runs and, recently, not-so-long runs are all a development of major economic significance. But in many other ways, and certainly in the long view of history, these developments are trivial. They are one more improvement in the state of the art of metalworking and fabrication.

Far more significant are developments in information theory, communications, and control. These have already led to some interesting and significant technology. For example:

1. The electronic computers, both digital and analog, which are being combined in some of the most advanced experimental applications, applied to mechanization of clerical work, and increasingly used to extend the range of man's capabilities in work hitherto impossible or badly performed by conventional techniques: long-range weather forecasting, air traffic control, and translating machines that scan printed documents, translate, abstract the translation, cross-index, store, and retrieve the translation.

2. Numerical control not only of machine tools but also of assembly machines and transfer devices, making possible flexible automatic systems adaptable to the varied products and short runs of the conventional production shop.

3. Computer control of process plants—power generation, petrochemical manufacture, steel rolling,

atomic facilities, pulp and paper manufacture—where start-up and monitoring, as well as automatic optimum operation, are for the first time permitted by use of a computerized communications and control system.

Common to these examples is the application of information technology. While "Detroit Automation" may be peripheral, control and information technology is at the heart of the truly significant part of the automation development. While its roots are far in the past—steering engines of ships, Watt's governor, Dutch windmills, Roman float control, Chinese chariot linkage systems—the technology of feedback applied on any wide scale is a phenomenon of our own times.

All great ideas are simple and never "new" in the sense of being created in a vacuum or first exemplified, but the self-conscious realization of the possible use and ramifications of an idea is. To say that the Greek playwrights and the Russian novelists educed and used many of Freudian concepts does not derogate from the newness of Freud's insights. To point to early Christian communal theories, or even to pre-Marxian historians who considered economic factors, does not vitiate the force of Marx's economic determinism. The theory of interchangeable parts was revolutionary regardless of whether any particular factory had used it, before Whitney, because after Whitney, this society became aware of its implications in the production of goods. So it is with the feedback principle. Historians do not have to search for particular mechanical devices to show its prior existence, for we are all aware of the interaction of our sense perceptions and brain—true feedback circuitry. What is new is our conscious awareness of the potentials of this idea, and what is revolutionary will be the effects of the application of this technology on our society. Thus, in looking at automation as a development in the history of technology, communication and control will be the core of what we, and future generations, will recognize to be the truly significant development.

Yet, even here we must back off still further, for it is not the technology that will be the historical significance of automation. If we adopt the long view of history, it is to the social change brought on by technology that we must look for the real meaning of our current technological revolution. This is the revolution, not the machines.

• *Our science of psychology will change.* The startling fact about computers, which play checkers, is not how well they play, but that they improve. The current work being done on information systems, programing, and computer language has already brought us to the threshold of a breakthrough in learning theory. We can only guess what such a breakthrough would mean in all phases of education.

• *Our art will change.* Art, whether Oriental or Renaissance, has depended on the patronage of the privileged and leisured few. When increased leisure becomes a commonplace and the average man has more discretionary energy as well as discretionary income, art may assume a very different place in our lives. One might say that the chrome on American cars was not a Detroit aberration, but a response to popular demand for art, for decoration, for beauty. (Let us assume that its present abatement heralds improved taste, but not the lessening of this demand.)

The mushrooming of arts and crafts courses and the do-it-yourself industries may foreshadow a more general need for esthetic creativity.

• *New international trade patterns will evolve.* The determinants of comparative advantage, the diversity of markets and supplies, and the disparity of economic development are changing rapidly today. In part, they reflected the specialization concepts of the Industrial Revolution. As the integrated systems concepts of automation, as well as the integrated communications and systems capabilities of this new technology, begin to pervade the economic scene, these older systems of trade will change.

We already see emerging what David Lilienthal calls the "multinational corporation"—not one company doing business in a foreign country, but an integrated international corporation, staffed and owned by different nationals.

• *Language barriers will weaken.* Mathematics and music have always been universal languages, but there have been few who speak them. With the spread of this new technology and the increasing use of mathematical models and techniques in business, government, and research, there will not only be more people conversant with the language of mathematics but thought, which has generally been limited by lingual structure, will be redirected, will become more precise and more comprehensive, through these new techniques. As lingual provincialism lessens, it is impossible to guess what catholicisms will emerge.

• *Our political outlook will change.* We have only to glance at the plethora of legislation growing out of the Industrial Revolution to know that this new industrial revolution will elicit a political response from our society. The child labor laws, wage, hour, and working condition regulations were evolved to protect workers from the excesses of the factory environment, but it will remain for automation to free them from the bondage of the machine. Such quasi-political institutions as labor unions were developed to meet the special needs of the factory worker, but now that our working force has shifted from the factory to the office, and the office functions are themselves changing, these institutions will have to change or new ones evolve to meet the special needs of the new working force.

Perhaps the problem of labor will shift from the prevention of exploitation to the insurance of utilization. Full employment, which we have viewed as an economic necessity, will have to be seen in psychological or cultural terms. A "featherbed" job that may meet the former need cannot fulfill the latter.

Deeper political changes will result that cannot yet be predicted. Jefferson's concept of democracy—with its basic tenet of "that government governs best which governs least"—presupposed an agrarian society. Our own evolution of government welfare responsibility followed the industrialization of our society. Now, as the need of production for survival is surpassed, as poverty and hunger become problems of civil rights and equal opportunity, our political concerns will shift—including the balance between individual liberty and social responsibility.

The magnitude of change in business organization that will be brought about by this new technology is far greater than most of us recognize. Today's business organization structure is a legacy of the first Industrial Revolution, in which specialization of labor was followed by mechanization around specialties. We are now in possession of technology that allows us to build information systems that transcend the compartmentalized structure of business organization. Much of the difficulty experienced in putting these new tools to work in recent years results from the fact that their use clashes with our fundamental organization system, a problem not yet recognized by many organizations.

We are today using this technology in only the most elementary manner. New techniques utilizing computer capabilities are just beginning to appear on the business scene: operations research—building mathematical models to solve business problems: simulation—using the computer to supply "what would happen if" answers to decision alternatives; gaming theory—planning in strategically competitive markets. These are but a few. The main shift in organization necessary to utilize these new techniques and systems capabilities will result from the integrated, as opposed to departmentalized, conception of the business enterprise.

• As production is increasingly controlled by a business-wide information system, through computer scheduling and actual factory control, the traditional office-plant distinction will require overhaul.

• The role of middle management will change as the function of allocation of recourses is performed by computers. Some predict the disappearance of middle management as a line function and the growth of a new staffing function—the analysis and continuing reappraisal of the computer models and of the assumptions on which they are based, in order to keep the system sensitive and receptive to change.

• The advances made in communications, among machines as well as people, now allow for direct, cheap, and immediate flow and feedback of information among any geographic points. Management, therefore, has a capacity never possible before to either centralize or decentralize its decision functions. Whether centralization is appropriate will vary with the situation, but the decision need no longer fall automatically to decentralization.

New techniques will be evolved to enable the effective management of scientific, technical, creative, and service personnel—an increasingly important determinant of business success. While the early part of the twentieth century saw an employment shift in the United States from the farm to the factory, the 1950's and 1960's brought a shift from the factory to the office. Even within manufacturing, the factory worker is being replaced by clerical, technical, and managerial employees.

Our methods of management have not kept pace with this shift. America has entered this era with a legacy of concepts developed to meet the needs of the *unskilled* worker. The results of labor-management relations to date might be summarized as the guarantee of equal treatment and the expectation of average performance. These concepts are already recognized as archaic in dealing with creative personnel. What must be encouraged is exceptional performance, and what may well be needed is individual treatment. The problems in this area are substantial and numerous. One is that the product, an idea, is so difficult to schedule; another is that scientists tend to direct their prime loyalty to their professions, rather than their employers; a third is the magnitude of the task of integrating what must remain an individual effort; and a fourth is the lack of standards to measure performance.

Studies in human relations have done much to give us insight into the human requirements of effective organization, but this falls short of what is needed. Too often management unconsciously assumes that spending a given percentage on research or creating fine working conditions will produce results. The perquisites of genius follow— they do not precede—the essence of genius, a fact that often is lost sight of. Fine equipment, campus-like plants, and company-paid university courses are but empty trappings if the human quality is not already present.

Few managements yet understand the essence of the task. The rewards of those who do will be greater as change increases. Thus, looking at automation as a historical development—while on the one hand leading us far afield from both automation and technology—not only helps put today's machines in perspective but gives some indication of the context in which tomorrow's technology will evolve and be put to work. The value of such perspective to business and to society cannot be overstated. Yet to many, even to most, it still appears an academic exercise, so difficult is it to think of a world that differs in any major way from that in which we live at the moment. Despite the centuries of looking back and the increasing rate of change that we see—now in decades rather than centuries or eons—we still find it difficult to look ahead. But this will change. And it is in the perspective of history that we will learn to educate ourselves for the future.

A TIME SCALE OF SCIENTIFIC AND TECHNOLOGICAL ACCELERATION

Another view of the processes of science and technology that have brought us to the present point of social change is provided by an examination of the increasingly short time-spans between the formulation of scientific theory and its practical applications over the past three centuries. This approach suffers from a number of problems: the difficulty of determining what, if any, cross-fertilization took place among the various scientific and technological innovators, the problem of arbitrary distinctions among disciplines and lines of progress.

The end papers of this book present the processes and problems graphically. They show the progressive telescoping of the time required for major scientific and technological developments to come to fruition since the mid-seventeenth century. But they also point to the dilemma. For instance, is it correct to place the work of Faraday under *electricity* and the work of Maxwell under *wireless transmission?* Perhaps computers should not be listed as a separate class, but only the theories of computation and the development of computer components, such as mechanical and electro-mechanical devices, vacuum tubes, transistors, and integrated circuitry. However, the dilemma itself demonstrates something important for evaluating past trends and future possibilities: scientific and technological innovation emerges from a pool of information, and the larger this pool, the greater the likelihood of its containing the specific scientific and technological data required for further advances. Thus, we can look at this time-scale with confidence that it indicates something of importance. At the very least, it is an analogy of the process central to the assumptions made here.

The time-scale shows some of the more important contributions to scientific and technological development. At first these contributions come singly and decades apart. Lately they have multiplied and have increased in frequency. We see that in the 200 years between the mid-seventeenth and mid-nineteenth centuries, the time between initial work and final, major application was cut at least in half. It took 160 years from Christian Huyghens' suggestion for an organized investigation of steam power to the beginning of the last major application, the steam locomotive. It took some 80 years from André Marie Ampère and Alessandro Volta to the installation of the first commercial electric power plant. If we add on a century of random experiments in steam that preceded Huyghens and some 50 years to include its application to the generation of electric power, we cut the ratio even further to 3 to 1.

Over the next 100 years, time was progressively cut again and again: 66 years from the work of Maxwell in 1873 to commercial television; 50 years from the discoveries of Max Planck and Albert Einstein at the beginning of the twentieth century to the peaceful application of atomic power; 15 years from Howard Aiken's start of construction on the first modern digital computer in 1939 to the first widespread commercial applications; 4 to 10 years from the invention of the transistor by Bardeen, Shockley, and Brattain at Bell Laboratories in 1948 to commercial applications in telephone communications, hearing aids and computers. Developments in cryogenics, in the new biology, and in laser technology are very recent but appear to follow the foreshortened time-scale of the other scientific and technological advances over the past 30 years.

Who are the individuals in the United States who are caught up in this process of change and contribute to it? Within ten years, the infants and young children of today will be in primary school or high school to learn how to cope with their changing environment. Those now leaving elementary school will be looking for work. In twenty years, the children of today's school children will be in elementary school. People now in their forties or fifties will be retiring by 1985, and those now infants will be going to college or preparing to enter the labor force. In the meantime, the population of the United States probably will have increased by some 75 million— that is, by more than one-third. All in all, therefore, the education and the labor turnover—those entering and leaving educational institutions and the labor market— over the next twenty years will involve an aggregate number of people almost as large as our current population of some 200 million.

This mass, with varying motivations, needs, and capabilities, represents the social material upon which the proliferation of scientific and technological advance will have its most immediate impacts. And to the possibilities of change inherent therein we must now bring to bear all the wisdom, all the morality, and all the nobility we can muster.

THE FUTURE

Man is challenged by two phenomena of his own making. He is challenged by two aspects of his technology, which stems from his ability, in the words of Julian Huxley, to "transmit experience cumulatively down the generations and incorporate its results directly into the evolutionary system." The nature of the problem is quite opposite to the one often cited—that the machine threatens to turn man into another machine. The real problem is that science is bringing about a situation that is forcing man to reconsider his role in relation to the fundamental forces of the universe.

• *Man's intellect no longer sets him apart from the rest of creation.* He has created machines that increasingly are able to think like and even out-think him. Already in existence are "heuristic" (goal-oriented) computers, which solve problems without being told how, by trial and error processes, which no longer can be differentiated meaningfully from what we know as human learning. Man has developed theories pointing to the almost certain existence of equal or superior intelligences elsewhere in the universe. Thus, man finds himself lacking in the self-imposed requisites for a unique place among the creatures of God. He neither has devised new requisites he is able to meet nor has he prepared himself to abdicate his unique place.

• *Man's physical form and psychological make-up have been freed from the imperceptible course directed by nat-*

ural evolution. The undirected or misdirected application of technology is threatening not only man's environment but the quality of future generations. At the same time, man's knowledge, his technology, can vastly accelerate, even bypass, the evolutionary process. Even now the creation of "cyborgs"—men with artificial organs—has begun. This, extended by the incipient ability to alter the blueprint of future generations through the manipulation of DNA (deoxyribonucleic acid), the basic genetic material, gives man the power to participate in and largely control the act of his own continual creation. But he has not decided if he should do so or to what end he should do so.

Clearly, both of these phenomena are accompanied by infinite dangers and by infinite opportunities. Yet the dangers can be overcome and the opportunities realized only by the development of the fundamental qualities that are inherent to some degree in every man—wisdom, morality, nobility. These cannot be built into a machine, and they alone can guide man toward worthy and valid goals, as he directs his own evolution.

Here, briefly, are some of the specifics of these challenges to man's self-conception and self-determination.

Cartesian reasoning led to this statement: *"Cogito, ergo sum."* I think; therefore I am. It tided us over many a rough stretch in the history of man's self-discovery. The earth is no longer the center of creation? Very well, but *"Cogito, ergo sum."* There are machines that work faster and better than my hands? Very well, but *"Cogito, ergo sum."* Adam was not molded out of clay one fine morning a few thousand years ago? Rationality does not con-

trol my every action, and something links me closely to
the dog burying his bone in the garden? But who or what
else can say, "I think; therefore I am"?

A few years ago, a cartoon in *The New Yorker* showed
two men standing in front of a computer about two stories
high and half a block long. One of the men was reading
the computer's print-out: *"Cogito, ergo sum."* It was quite
funny, a few years ago. But we have seen over the past
decade the development of technologies and theories that
range from cryogenics and molectronics to the simulation
of rudimentary mental processes. Applied, through what
James T. Culbertson, in his study *The Minds of Robots,*
calls the mathematical biophysics of the nervous system,
they enable us to construct machines that react to problems
in a manner fundamentally indistinguishable from the
reactions of human intelligence.

What has happened is simple to understand. Technological advance has become self-generating. To borrow a
phrase from the economic terminology for developing
countries, technology has reached the "take-off point."
No longer must technological progress wait on the next
individual scientific discovery; technology itself is pushing
research into new discoveries and new dimensions. Thus,
the computer is throwing off whole new families of machines—process controls, translating machines, design
computers, communications switching equipment, special
purpose systems, and so forth—developed through calculations made possible by the computer itself.

Of course, much more is involved than mere information technology. For the direct result of man's increasing
control and manipulation of knowledge is man's ability

to produce materials, shape forms, test hypotheses, monitor events, and reach conclusions leading to the creation of "cyborgs" and the determination of genetic patterns, and catapulting him from his earthbound physical and intellectual base to the rim or core of universal creation. Nonetheless, to a large extent the essential starting point for these things is the growing scope of the computer.

The enormous scale of this expansion of capabilities has been discussed in the previous chapters and need not be restated here. Suffice it to say that it is the result of the miniaturization of computer components, new materials, temperature control, and other techniques. This expansion, in turn, makes possible the development of goal-oriented computers. This is called heuristics and represents the essence of machine intelligence.

A computer is given a goal, such as winning a checker game or optimizing the profit of an enterprise. It also is given a limited amount of fundamental data—some, but not all, of the rules of checkers or certain economic, market, and operating information. Continually added are new data—the moves of the opposing player or market declines, the introduction of competitive products and other factors. The computer, making billions of calculations in seconds, chooses one alternative after another. The routes of calculations leading to success are re-enforced—stored in the memory—even as better procedures are being tried by the computer, and even as new data representing new obstacles or opportunities are fed into the system. The computer devises its own strategy in pursuit of the goal.

This is the way computers have defeated the men who

taught them checkers. This is the way they can be used in business or war gaming. This is the way, eventually, that they will accomplish space explorations too dangerous for men to undertake and, even, seek out objectives men do not know exist.

In developing heuristic machines, man in the not too distant future will be faced by the fact that creatures of his invention are able to reach solutions not only faster than he, as is already the case, but by means that would take many lifetimes for man to understand. This will be in addition to the fact that probability theory points to the existence of intelligent creatures in thousands of places within the universe. Man's computers may well provide the opportunity and the means for communicating with these other intelligences, many of them undoubtedly superior to ours. What, then, will be man's place in the hierarchy of being? Creatures of his own making may surpass him in what he always has done best on earth. His reason tells him that creatures elsewhere equal or excel him. Does *thinking* make them *be,* in the way man is? Perhaps. But perhaps also it does not matter, if man turns an inward look on man, competing with neither angels nor computers but only with himself to excel his past and stretch his potential.

Julian Huxley, in *The Future of Man: Evolutionary Aspects,* wrote:

> To me it is an exciting fact that man, after he appeared to have been dethroned from his supremacy, demoted from his central position in the universe to the status of an insignificant inhabitant of a small outlying planet of one among millions of stars, has now become reinstated in a key position, one of

the rare spearheads or torchbearers, or trustees—choose your metaphor according to taste!—of advance in the cosmic process of evolution.

Actually, there are two possibilities with regard to man's use of his knowledge. On the one hand, by the conscious but misdirected application of technology—through "death control" unbalanced by birth control—not only is man endangering the welfare of future generations on an overcrowded planet, but he already has set in motion a gradual decline in the over-all genetic quality of the human race. Probably he also has caused a certain number of potentially debilitating mutations by nuclear fallout and, perhaps, by chemical means. Another cartoon comes to mind: a bearded white-robed figure was carrying a placard on a crowded city street; cars and people were rushing by; the placard read: "The world ended *yesterday.*"

On the other hand, man has the opportunity to apply his increasing knowledge of genetics and life processes and his vastly expanded mathematical capabilities to the task of accelerating the natural process of evolution toward what Huxley calls "higher levels of mental or psychological activity." While man has all the information to opt successfully for destruction, he also has the capability to assimilate this information in the triumphant pursuit of the second course, a capability provided by the advances in information technology (computers), which can cope with the vast, scattered resources of knowledge that literally are doubling every ten years.

In essence, however, the choice made by man will not be made on the basis of intellect. If it were, the result would be certain. And this is far from the case. What will direct man's choice? And, should he choose to grasp the opportunity of self-betterment, what will be his instruments and what will determine his particular goals? Winston Churchill warned that "the dark ages may return on the gleaming wings of science." This would be the outcome of an undisciplined technology. Man can do what man wants. The selection of means and ends can either call forth his essential qualities or plunge him into ignominy unparalleled in the catalogue of human cruelty and folly.

Indeed, we dare not deceive ourselves—we and our children and children's children. Only the essential qualities of man's character—wisdom, morality, nobility—can tip the balance against the self-pity brought by knowledge and against the choice between chaos and tyranny conjured up by science and technology. These qualities are not granted to races or nations. They are not possessed only by leaders. The fundamental choices of today are not rational or ideological in the traditional sense. They are cosmic and, therefore, individual. They must be made by individuals in terms of their responsibilities to the future of man.

It is not the task, therefore, of today's leadership, especially the educational leadership, to try to mold what J. B. S. Haldane called "fanatical devotees of Mary, Marx, Muhammed, or Mammon." They probably would not succeed. Too many men know too much. But if they did succeed, their pupils would not be equipped to seek answers to the questions of man's survival.

Perhaps, instead, there could be created an institute for

the continual assessment of the human consequences of technological change. Such an institute might be national at first but could be planned along international, universal, lines. It must not be exclusive, but inclusive. It must not discourage the duplication of effort, but must foster as many attempts to find answers to as many questions, or variations of the same questions, as possible. It must be a center not of authority, but of inquiry. It must provide focus, but leave no area of investigation deliberately shut off. Above all, such an institute should try to assess not only the immediate and obvious consequences of automation and related developments but the impact of accelerated change itself. The whole tenor of life has been altered over the past three generations by the fact of change. The young man who in 1900 looked into his future as a physician, mechanic, or farmer thought he saw before him a landscape brightened by historical precedent and family experience. Even he was quite certain to be disappointed. His son was less sure, but if he was sure, his disappointment was more certain.

In the last generation, technology has overwhelmed the general practitioner, obliterated the mechanic's machine, forced the family farm into huge agricultural combines. Even though these technological manifestations were startling enough—in terms of hospitals, communications, production, economics, nations swept away, empires and ideologies born—their fundamental human importance resides in the fact of change itself. For what do the young men and women of today know of the future? The future will be change, and this change will be of unprecedented speed and variety. Does this knowledge drive them to noncommitment, to the simplistic life of the youth gang, to "kicks," to despair, to hope, to a gathering of resources for the assault? What has the condition of accelerating change done to their parents and grandparents? How many human values lie rotting on the junk heap of frustration and fear? The answers to these questions lie in the study of the consequences of change.

It is not useful to point to any one existing type of institution to do this kind of job. Each has heritages of past conflicts of interest, and past criticism, justified or not. Of course, there are the great foundations. There is the unique venture of IBM, which set up at Harvard University in 1964 the Program on Technology and Society. Three years later, at Columbia University, the Alfred P. Sloan Foundation and IBM financed the establishment of the Institute for the Study of Science in Human Affairs. A number of similar efforts are being undertaken at other universities and under other auspices. Yet without detracting from the credit these programs merit and without being presumptuous, it should be possible to ask for something newer, more definitive, more direct in meeting the needs of the future. Perhaps it could take the form of a joint effort among these programs. But, possibly, this is too disingenuous a suggestion.

There is no final word on the future; the nature of the concept precludes it. Here, indicated by example is how we have arrived at the threshold we are about to cross. This is not a book of prophecy. Perhaps, more than anything, it is an expression of the limited optimism that reason still permits us, many experiences to the contrary.

This neutral kind of confidence allows us to hope that science and technology ultimately will be put in the service of man, that their profound impact on the world will be beneficial. There is hope in the words of William Shakespeare: "What a piece of work is a man! how noble in reason! how infinite in faculty! in form and moving how express and admirable! in action how like an angel! in apprehension how like a god!"

SELECTED READINGS

Most of the books on this list have been published within the past fifteen years. They present facts, ideas, and serious philosophical discussions on the pervasive impact of science and technology on individuals, institutions, and societies. The reader has here a list of books that can help him make up his mind on issues of central importance to the future of man in a world of accelerating change.

Barzun, Jacques. *Science: The Glorious Entertainment.* New York: Harper & Row, 1964.

——. *The American University: How It Runs, Where It Is Going.* New York: Harper & Row, 1968.

Blitz, Herbert J., ed. *Labor-Management Contracts and Technological Change: Case Studies and Contract Clauses.* Diebold Institute Studies in Public Policy. New York: Praeger, 1969.

Boulding, Kenneth E. *The Meaning of the 20th Century: The Great Transition.* New York: Harper & Row, 1964.

Bowles, Edmund A., ed. *Computers in Humanistic Research: Readings and Perspectives.* Englewood Cliffs, N.J.: Prentice-Hall, 1967.

Brady, Robert A. *Organization, Automation, and Society: The Scientific Revolution in Industry.* Berkeley, Calif.: Univ. of California Press, 1961.

Bronowski, J. *Science and Human Values.* New York: Harper & Row, 1965.

————. *The Identity of Man*. Published for the American Museum of Natural History. Garden City, N.Y.: Natural History Press, 1965.

Bush, Vannevar. *Science Is Not Enough: Reflections for the Present and Future*. New York: Morrow, 1967.

————. *Science: The Endless Frontier*. Washington, D.C.: National Science Foundation, 1960.

Clarke, Arthur C. *Profiles of the Future: An Inquiry into the Limits of the Possible*. New York: Harper & Row, 1962.

Commoner, Barry. *Science and Survival*. New York: Viking Press, 1966.

Coombs, Philip H. *The World Educational Crisis: A Systems Analysis*. New York: Oxford Univ. Press, 1968.

Diebold, John. *Beyond Automation: Managerial Problems of an Exploding Technology*. New York: McGraw-Hill, 1964.

Dobzhansky, Theodosius. *The Biology of Ultimate Concern*. New York: New American Library, 1967.

Dunlop, John T., ed. *Automation and Technological Chance*. Englewood Cliffs, N.J.: Prentice-Hall, 1962.

Gardner, John W. *No Easy Victories*. New York: Harper & Row, 1968.

Ginzberg, Eli, ed. *Technology and Social Change*. New York: Columbia Univ. Press, 1964.

Glass, Hiram B. *Science and Ethical Values*. Chapel Hill, N.C.: Univ. of North Carolina Press, 1965.

Haskins, Caryl P. *The Scientific Revolution and World Politics*. Published for the Council on Foreign Relations. New York: Harper & Row, 1964.

Hoyle, Fred. *Of Men and Galaxies*. Seattle: Univ. of Washington Press, 1964.

Kahn, Herman, and Wiener, Anthony J. *The Year 2000: A Framework for Speculation on the Next Thirty-three Years*. New York: Macmillan, 1967.

Keppel, Francis. *The Necessary Revolution in American Education*. New York: Harper & Row, 1966.

Klemm, Friedrich. *A History of Western Technology*. Translated by Dorothea Waley Singer. New York: Scribners, 1959.

Morison, Elting E. *Men, Machines, and Modern Times.* Cambridge, Mass.: M.I.T. Press, 1966.

Prehoda, Robert. *Designing the Future: The Role of Technological Forecasting.* Philadelphia: Chilton, 1967.

Price, Derek J. de Solla. *Little Science, Big Science.* New York: Columbia Univ. Press, 1963.

Ridgeway, James. *The Closed Corporation: American Universities in Crisis.* New York: Random House, 1968.

Schwebel, Milton. *Who Can Be Educated.* New York: Grove Press, 1968.

Servan-Schreiber, J. J. *The American Challenge.* New York: Atheneum, 1968.

Skolnikoff, Eugene B. *Science, Technology, and American Foreign Policy.* Cambridge, Mass.: M.I.T. Press, 1967.

Sonneborn, Tracy M., ed. *The Control of Human Heredity and Evolution.* New York: Macmillan, 1965.

Taylor, Gordon Rattray. *The Biological Time Bomb.* Cleveland: World, 1968.

Technomics, Inc. *Computer System Support for Comprehensive Educational Advancement.* Santa Monica, Calif.: Technomics, 1966.

Trow, William C. *Teacher and Technology.* New York: Appleton-Century-Crofts, 1963.

U.S. Office of Education. *A Supplementary Report: Computer Assisted Instruction.* Prepared by General Learning Corp., 1968.

Weaver, Warren. *Science and Imagination.* New York: Basic Books, 1967.

Wiener, Norbert. *God & Golem Inc.: A Comment on Certain Points Where Cybernetics Impinges on Religion.* Cambridge, Mass.: M.I.T. Press, 1964.

————. *The Human Use of Human Beings: Cybernetics and Society.* Garden City, N.Y.: Doubleday, 1954.

Wolstenholme, Gordon, ed. *Man and His Future.* Boston: Little, Brown, 1963.

Wooldridge, Dean E. *Mechanical Man: The Physical Basis of Intelligent Life.* New York: McGraw-Hill, 1968.

1666

STEAM

1666

ELECTRICITY

1800

STEAM

160 years from Huyghens to the first steam railroad

1666   The suggestion of Christian Huyghens, after nearly a century of random, widely separated experiments by different individuals, of an organized investigation of steam power in France.

1690   Denis Papin's publication of first design for steam engine.

1707   Papin's formulation of complete theory of steam engine.

1711-22   Thomas Newcomen's experiments with steam engines.

1769   James Watt's patent of steam engine.

1774-78   Installation of steam engines in Boulton's Soho works.

1807   Robert Fulton's steamboat.

1825   George Stephenson's steam railroad.

ELECTRICITY

80 years from Ampere and Volta to installation of first commercial power plant.

1800   Andre Marie Ampere's work in electrodynamics and Alessandro Volta's development of theory of current electricity.

1820   Hans Christian Oersted's observations of electromagnetism.

1827   George Ohm's law on relationship between intensity of electric currents and resistance.

1831   Karl Friedrich Gauss' and Wilhelm Weber's basic research in electricity and magnetism.

1831   Michael Faraday's discovery of electromagnetic induction.

1837   Samuel F. B. Morse's electro-magnetic recording telegraph.

1856-66   Laying of transatlantic telegraph cables.

1866-67   Development of commercial electric generators.

1871   Hermann Helmholtz work in electro-dynamics.

1876   Alexander Graham Bell's telephone.

1879   Thomas A. Edison's electric lamp.

1882   Installation of first commercial power plant.

WIRELESS TRANSMISSION

66 years from Maxwell to commercial television.

1873   James Maxwell's work with electro-magnetic waves.

1886   Heinrich Hertz's proof and developr of Maxwell's work.

1900   Guglielmo Marconi's developmen short wave communications.

1904-06   Sir John Fleming's invention of ra tubes.

1906   Lee de Forest's development of ra telephone.

1920   Opening of commercial radio station

1925   John L. Baird's and Charles F. Jenk demonstrations of television.

1939   Opening of commercial television stat

ATOMIC POWER

50 years from Planck and Einstei first nuclear powered ship.

1900-05   Max Planck's and Albert Einstein's mulations of theories underlying nuc fission.

1937   Otto Hahn's and Fritz Strassmann's periments in nuclear fission.

1941   Self-sustaining nuclear reaction.

1945   Nuclear explosion.

1952   Thermo-nuclear explosion.

1954   "Nautilus," nuclear reactor driven marine.

1956   Atomic power plant, Calder Hall, Engl

1958   "Savannah," atomic powered merc ship.

THE COMPUTER

Experiments with computers go b to the work of Leibnitz and, more cently, Babbage. But the first work analog computer was built by V nevar Bush in 1925. Thirty years la digital computers began to be use a significant extent for commer purposes.

1939   Initiation of construction on digital c puter.

1944   Completion of Mark I, first modern c tal computer.

1946   Completion of ENIAC, all-electronic c tal computer.

1954   Significant commercial applications electronic digital computer.

THE TRANSISTOR

Since its invention by Bardeen, Sho ley and Brattain, the transistor revolutionized the world of electron and has made possible many of